A guide to managing coastal erosion in beach/dune systems

SCOTTISH NATURAL HERITAGE AND COASTAL EROSION

Most beaches in Scotland are inherently dynamic in character and are subject to periodic coastal erosion. Along with sediment transport and deposition, this erosion is necessary for the creation, conservation and integrity of many of our unique coastal habitats, landforms and landscapes. As far as is possible within the constraints of public safety, Scottish Natural Heritage advocates approaches to erosion management which retain the natural coastal habitats, processes and landscapes and which enable Scotland's coastlines to evolve naturally with minimal human intervention.

Preface

Sandy beaches and dunes are an attractive and valuable element of Scotland's natural heritage. They are important for informal recreation and amenity, for nature conservation and, of course, as the basis of the country's renowned golf links. They are also highly dynamic landforms, susceptible to erosion and change which may threaten those developments and land uses sited nearest the sea.

This Guide does not offer 'solutions' to coastal erosion. The most appropriate response in each situation will differ, depending upon various factors such as the nature and value of the asset at risk, the coastal processes affecting the site and the area's nature conservation interests.

Instead, it reviews the options available for managing erosion, from non-intervention through to construction of revetments and seawalls, and offers guidance on how to select or design the most appropriate response to a particular situation. Critically, it describes and illustrates how each technique might best be designed so as to minimise damage to the natural heritage and reduce the prospects of altering shoreline evolution elsewhere.

Through it, Scottish Natural Heritage seeks to encourage coastal authorities and managers to implement approaches to erosion management which maintain the important and varied conservation interests of Scotland's unique beach and dune systems.

The Guide was prepared for Scottish Natural Heritage by HR Wallingford. The Project Manager for HR Wallingford was Mr Tom Coates. Contributing authors were Dr Alan Brampton, Mr George Motyka and Mr Tom Coates. The SNH Project Officer was Dr George Lees.

October 2000.

Contents

Tables

Figures

Appendices

5

1. Introduction

Dunes are an important feature of Scotland's coastline. They range in character from the pocket beaches and machair systems of the wet and wind-swept north-west coasts *(Plate 1)*, to the long, broad belts of dunes on the east and south-west coasts that are so favoured for golf links *(Plate 2)*. The distribution of dunes around the Scottish coast is illustrated in Figure 1.

Dune systems are usually fronted by sand beaches, more rarely by beaches of gravel and sand. Many of the major dune areas were originally formed several thousand of years ago from sand produced by the action of glaciers and delivered to the coast by rivers in the last Ice Age. As sea level rose to approximately its present level the sand was driven onshore and formed into dunes by onshore winds. Continual modification by waves, tides and winds has produced the situation found today. Under natural conditions dunes undergo periods of growth and erosion with each process contributing to their dynamic evolution. It is only when the coastal area becomes developed for recreation, housing, transport, industry or military facilities that these natural processes are perceived as problems needing to be managed.

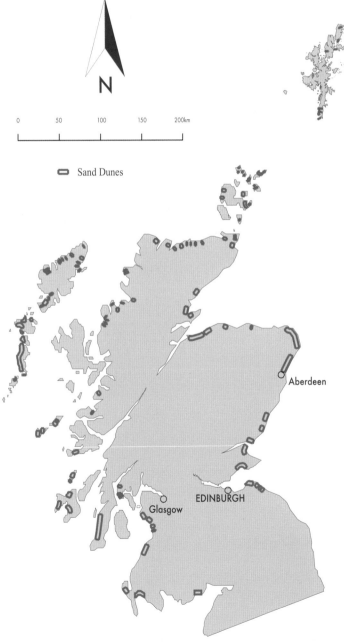

Figure 1   Location of major Scottish dune systems

From the perspective of coastal management dunes protect low lying coastal areas from flooding and also act as a buffer against erosion: they form a reservoir of sand, replenished when beach levels are high and released to nourish the foreshore during storm erosion. They are also areas of considerable scientific, conservation, landscape and recreational value. Because of these attributes they are important to a wide range of human activities, and their management is seen as an important objective in planning and usage of the coastal zone. Unfortunately, there has been a long history of poor management of coastal dunes, with unnecessary, expensive and unattractive engineering works having been undertaken that have often caused more problems than they have solved. Present day dune management in Scotland is undertaken by various groups, including local land owners, golf clubs, the Unitary Councils, Scottish Natural Heritage and the Ranger Service.

This Guide summarises the natural processes that build and erode dunes and discusses the impacts of human activities. The Guide then describes methods for the management of marine erosion, with an emphasis on methods that cause minimum disruption to natural dune evolution while still providing acceptable protection to the assets at risk. **There is an underlying assumption that natural erosion of dunes is not a problem in itself, and that erosion normally only needs to be controlled to protect human assets at risk.** Both the long-term and short-term perspectives on processes and management are considered. References are provided to complementary publications that describe the prevention and repair of erosion caused by wind action and people.

Scottish Natural Heritage (SNH) commissioned this Guide to assist in the practical management of marine erosion along dunes and beaches. It is written for use by all organisations and individuals involved in the practical management of coastal dune systems in Scotland, including Local Authorities, coastal consultants, the Ranger Service, landowners and golf course managers.

The Guide is not intended to provide an in depth view of coastal processes, as this subject is covered in numerous texts (see for example the Beach Management Manual, CIRIA, 1996). Nor is it intended to cover the well documented methods for the prevention or repair of damage to dunes caused by wind action, recreation or grazing (see for example the Sand Dunes Handbook, BTCV, 1996). However the Guide does recognise that management of marine erosion of dunes will often need to be carried out in combination with protection or repair of damage from other causes.

In preparing this Guide the authors visited a number of dune systems around Scotland, observing different erosion control schemes and discussing the surrounding issues with landowners, engineers, Rangers, SNH staff and recreational users of the shoreline. The authors have also reviewed UK and international literature on dune erosion and management.

The text starts with a brief description of the interactions between dunes, beaches and the sea, considering both the long-term evolution of coastal dunes in Scotland and the shorter-term changes. The many attributes of dunes, and the different perspectives that people have of them are discussed. These attributes need to be considered before undertaking any management operations, particularly if sustainable and environmentally acceptable solutions are to be devised. The responsibilities and powers of various authorities that may be involved in coastal protection or dune management schemes in Scotland are briefly summarised. Discussion then moves on to erosion management from a strategic perspective. Finally an overview is presented of the various management approaches available and a guide provided on the selection of the most appropriate methods for a given site.

The References and Bibliography include a wide range of entries that are intended to provide useful further reading. Included are regional references to the Scottish coast, guidance for dune management operations and useful background reading on coastal processes. A glossary of terms and abbreviations is included.

The remainder of the Guide is given over to Appendices, comprising:

1. A set of stand alone summaries that describe potential erosion management approaches with sufficient information to assess applicability to specific sites and to get small projects underway. The summaries concentrate on those approaches that are low cost and will have limited impact on the environment, coastal recreation and the landscape. Major coast protection schemes are not covered in any detail as it is assumed that they would be designed by competent engineers with the support of specialists; in these cases the summaries only provide sufficient information to assist readers in assessing proposed schemes at the planning stage and to help identify elements of good practice that these schemes should embrace.

2. A discussion of methods for monitoring coastal erosion and change in dune systems, using either low cost observational techniques or specialist techniques and measurements. Protocols and proformas are included for low cost techniques.

2. Dunes, beaches and the sea

Plate 1
Typical Highland beach-dune system, Strathy.

Dunes are a dynamic, but fragile coastal landform. The interactions between dunes and beaches lie at the heart of this manual. The changes brought about by the natural processes of winds, waves and tides are rarely gradual or predictable. Rather they are episodic, with periods of little or no change followed by times of intense activity, most obviously during storms when dunes may be eroded rapidly, their seaward faces receding many metres in a few days. Often these events go unnoticed by local residents or land-owners, with subsequent re-building of the dunes by wind action in the following weeks and months. However, when damage occurs with little or no natural restoration of the dunes over a period of several years, then concern arises, especially if there are important assets at risk to the landward *(Plate 2)*. It is usually as a result of such events that intervention works are undertaken, sometimes later proving to be unnecessary or damaging to the natural beach/ dune system.

Plate 2
Sustained coastal erosion has affected Montrose golf course in recent years.

2.1 Long-term evolution of dunes

2.1.1 Sources of sand for dunes

Most dunes in Scotland are formed from sand produced and delivered to the coast by glaciers, or rivers draining from them. This means that the major source of sand started to decline about 10,000 years ago at the end of the last Ice Age, and has now virtually disappeared. Present day supplies of sand are modest in comparison. The generally hard rocks forming cliffs and the nearshore seabed around much of Scotland yield little fresh sand for the beaches. Some rivers in Scotland still supply sand to the coastline, although much of this settles out in estuaries rather than travelling directly to the open coast.

Plate 3
White calcareous sand beach, Lingay Strand, N Uist.

In many areas, the only new sand for beaches and dunes is derived from broken shells *(Plate 3)*. This serves a double purpose, firstly replacing sand lost from the beaches and dunes and secondly providing minerals that are taken up by the dune vegetation, encouraging growth and therefore sand stabilisation and retention.

Plate 4
Little fresh sand is being added to Scotland's beaches today. Sand or shingle removed from beaches is not replaced naturally and can lead to beach lowering and subsequent dune erosion.

2.1.2　Losses of sand from dunes

Sand is continually being lost from the open coast. Waves transport beach material into more sheltered areas (e.g. estuaries) or carry it offshore, to settle out on the seabed. In addition wave action slowly abrades even the hardest pebbles and sand grains, with the very fine particles being carried away by winds or currents either to seaward or landward. The rate of sand loss from beaches in Scotland generally exceeds the supply of new sand and results in long term landward retreat.

A further cause of long-term shoreline retreat is the rise in mean sea level relative to the land. In recent centuries, Scotland has not greatly suffered from the increase in global sea levels, which has been averaging about 1mm to 1.5mm/year. This is because much of mainland Scotland is itself increasing in elevation as the landmass recovers isostatically from the superimposed weight of the ice laid over it during the last Ice Age. In the western Highlands of Scotland, this process is still occurring faster than the increase in sea level, leading to a nett local lowering of sea level relative to the coastline. Elsewhere in Scotland the rate of global sea level rise now matches or exceeds that of the landmass, with a resultant nett increase in local sea levels. As sea level rises relative to a beach, there is an inevitable tendency for the shoreline to move inland.

In the future, the consequences of atmospheric pollution, and hence global warming, may include an acceleration of the increase in mean sea levels around the world. As a consequence, large parts of the coast of Scotland may begin to experience, for the first time in thousands of years, a nett increase in sea levels. In other areas, the existing rate of sea level rise may substantially increase.

2.1.3 Consequences for dune evolution

Most dunes in Scotland can be expected to retreat in the long-term, as a result of both a general loss of the existing sand and in response to beach retreat under the influence of sea level rise.

There are, however, exceptions to the general trend of long-term erosion. There are some sandy beach/ dune areas around the coast of Scotland that have been gaining sediment and advancing seawards. Usually, the sand that is accumulating in these areas has been removed from other parts of the coastline (often from dune erosion), and carried along the beaches by longshore drift. This long-term re-distribution process typically occurs where sand has been deposited in large dune systems thousands of years ago, when sea levels and wave conditions would have been very different from those of today. Erosion of these ancient dune systems may continue indefinitely, with the sand they lose being transported and deposited elsewhere along the coastline, often leading to the creation of new dunes.

In the vicinity of river mouths, tidal inlets or estuaries, other redistribution mechanisms are at work. The combination of wave action and tidal currents will transfer sand from one side of an estuary to another. In some cases, they also remove sediments from inside the estuary and deposit it outside on the open coastline to produce new dunes. Elsewhere, the opposite process occurs: beaches and dunes outside the estuary mouth erode, and the sand they lose travels into the estuary, slowly filling it.

Overall, the long-term pattern of evolution of sandy beaches and dunes in Scotland is of loss of sand and a general landward retreat. Where beaches and dunes are gaining sand, then this is almost always at the expense of beach and dune erosion elsewhere along the coast. Even these gains might prove transient as the processes leading to growth may well change, resulting in rapid erosion of the accumulated sand.

2.2 Short-term dune evolution processes

The long-term patterns of dune evolution described above, although producing underlying trends of change, are often difficult to detect because of substantial and rapid changes in dunes in the short-term (i.e. over days or weeks). It is usually severe short-term erosion events, occurring either singly or cumulatively over a few years, that cause concern and lead to attempts to influence the natural processes.

Plate 5
Beach-dune systems undergo cyclical changes in appearance due to broadly seasonal weather patterns. Under fairweather conditions, sand collects on the upper beach and dune face. When storms occur this is removed, giving the dunes an eroded appearance even though there may not be any long-term erosional trend.

Dunes are dynamic landforms that respond to changing conditions along the coast, usually brought about by the varying weather. Coastal dunes accumulate sand blown inland from the beaches in front of them by onshore winds (accretion). They lose sand by a variety of mechanisms, divided here into two main classes:

● deflation caused by winds
● marine erosion caused mainly by waves.

The main concerns about dunes usually arise when it is perceived that the erosion processes have removed more sand than the accretion processes can replace over time scales of months or a few years and this erosion threatens developed areas, infrastructure, commercial interests or important natural assets. Problems can also arise when accretion dominates, because the excess of sand blows inland affecting agriculture, blocking roads or even inundating built up areas. Natural erosion or accretion of undeveloped dune systems is not normally considered to be a problem, but rather an integral part of geomorphological evolution. A brief description of the accretion and erosion processes is set out below.

2.2.1   Accretion of dunes

The basic requirements for the formation of coastal dunes are:

- a supply of sand over a wide drying foreshore
- a backshore area of low relief
- predominant onshore winds for at least part of the year.

Dunes usually begin to form at the crest of a beach, with wind-blown sand accumulating around small objects such as clumps of seaweed, driftwood or other debris cast up along the strand line. Once formed, the low hills of loose sand are colonised by salt-tolerant, pioneer plants that both increase the resistance of the surface layer of sand to wind erosion and reduce the wind speeds over the surface (*Plate 6*). The embryo dunes or foredunes will continue growing, unless they are destroyed by wave action at high tide levels.

Plate 6
Sand accretion on backshore fixed by sea-lyme and marram grass to form embryo dunes.

In Scotland the main pioneering colonisers of loose sand include sand couchgrass (*Elymus farctus*) and lyme grass (*Leymus arenarius*). They are able to withstand short periods of immersion by seawater and have long roots, rhizomes and runners, which help to bind the surface grains and extend the vegetative cover laterally. As the foredunes grow vertically above the level of wave run up, they are colonised by marram grass (*Ammophila arenaria*), which thrives on continual burial by the blown sand deposits. The marram dominated dunes remain unstable and are known as yellow dunes due to the exposure of sand between the clumps of vegetation. If new foredunes develop to windward of the yellow dunes, the marram ceases to be supplied with fresh sand deposits, and other species colonise and stabilise the dune surface. Lichens typically carpet the surface between other species, often giving the dunes a grey appearance and hence the name grey dunes. The composition of the ultimate vegetation cover will vary depending on the soil chemistry, with the calcium rich sands of some parts of Scotland giving rise to species-rich grasslands. Where strong winds and gales regularly influence the dune system sand may be blown some distance inshore, forming the machairs typical of the Western Isles.

The rate of dune vegetation growth depends on the climatic conditions, with growth in some regions being inhibited by low rainfall and extreme temperatures. Around Scotland's coastline, however, the wet and windy weather generally allows rapid and vigorous growth of dune vegetation.

Ideal conditions for the transport of sand from a beach to the dunes occur after constructive (i.e. low height, long period) waves have deposited sand on the upper beach and inter-tidal foreshore. At low tide the sand dries and onshore winds can carry substantial volumes of sand onto the dunes. The transport of sand is diminished if the sand is wet due to rain or ground water drainage and can be prevented entirely if winds are too weak to mobilise the grains or are blowing offshore.

The vertical growth of dunes can be curtailed by one of three factors, namely:

- The dune reaches a height where the vegetation is no longer able to protect the dune surface from wind erosion. In some parts of the world, coastal dunes can reach over 50m above sea level. In Scotland, the winter wind speeds this high above the sea surface can be very strong, and dunes rarely reach more than about 25m in height.
- New foredunes intercept a large proportion of the wind-blown sand, preventing the further growth of yellow or grey dunes. This situation occurs on prograding coasts, and may result in the formation of many dune ridges over the years. A good example is found along the coastline north of Aberdeen at Balmedie where the dunes extend over 250m inland of the present beach crest.
- Damage is caused to the dune vegetation by human influences (trampling, groundwater extraction, farming, construction, etc.) or by animal grazing/burrowing, hence diminishing the capacity of vegetation to trap and retain further sand.

The presence of a wide belt of dunes means that there has been a period of accretion in the past. However, this does not mean that the accretion is continuing. Lines of dunes set back from the beach may have originally formed many centuries ago, but there are sites in Scotland where these ancient dune systems are being eroded, re-distributing the sand in them to other parts of the coastline. Examples of these changes can be seen at Morrich More near Tain and the Eden estuary side of the golf links at St Andrews.

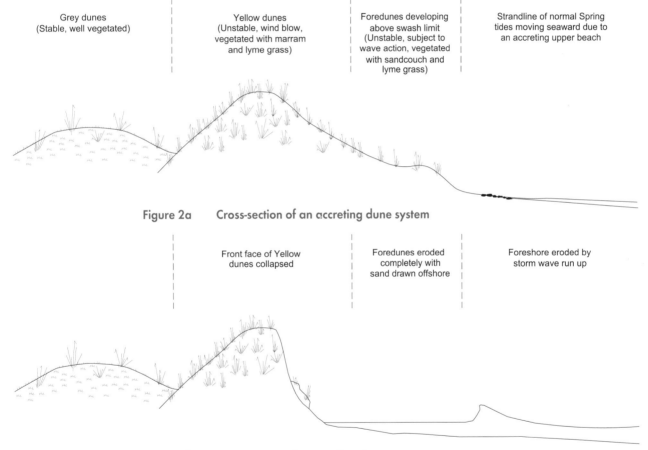

Grey dunes
(Stable, well vegetated)

Yellow dunes
(Unstable, wind blow,
vegetated with marram
and lyme grass)

Foredunes developing
above swash limit
(Unstable, subject to
wave action, vegetated
with sandcouch and
lyme grass)

Strandline of normal Spring
tides moving seaward due to
an accreting upper beach

Figure 2a   Cross-section of an accreting dune system

Front face of Yellow
dunes collapsed

Foredunes eroded
completely with
sand drawn offshore

Foreshore eroded by
storm wave run up

Figure 2b   Cross-section of an eroding dune system

2.2.2   Dune erosion

There are two main types of dune erosion, namely:

- Surface erosion by wind action (deflation)
- Marine erosion of the toe and seaward face of the dunes.

The former can and does occur naturally, following disease or damage to vegetation caused, for example, by drought, lack of nutrients or over-grazing by rabbits. However, the onset and subsequent problems of deflation are often worsened by human activities. Typical causes include excessive trampling, driving vehicles over dunes, the removal of sand for building materials or agricultural use, excessive extraction of ground water, and allowing excessive grazing by farm animals. If the vegetation is seriously damaged, it no longer acts to stabilise

Plate 7

Dune blowout, Harris. As the name implies such features are formed by wind scour rather than wave attack.

the sand and wind action will rapidly remove the exposed loose sand, forming a blow out *(Plate 7)*. Once initiated, a blow out can spread rapidly and large areas of dunes can be affected, to the extent that blown sand becomes a major nuisance further inland. There are numerous manuals and handbooks explaining how to repair and prevent further damage caused by deflation (for example BTCV, 1996). The methods include fencing, installing boardwalks, protection of the eroded dune surface by "thatching" and transplanting dune stabilising grasses.

This Guide concentrates on erosion of dunes caused by marine processes *(Plate 8)*. A typical sequence of events leading to erosion of the front face of dunes is as follows:

- Beach profiles in front of the dunes become flatter as a result of destructive wave action (large waves generated by local onshore winds).
- The upper beach levels fall, allowing the high tide mark to reach the toe of dunes.
- Waves impact directly onto the dune toe, causing sand to be removed and under-cutting the dune face.
- The front face of the dune collapses onto the beach, and the sand is carried down the beach.

Plate 8

Active marine erosion of dunes at Cruden Bay.

The consequence of such events is that the front face of the dune retreats, but the beach profile receives an additional volume of sand. Hence the dunes can act as a temporary reservoir of sand, accumulating it during mild weather, typically during the summer, and surrendering it back to the beach during storms. The erosion of a dune during a storm event, or several such events, may provide enough sand for the beach profile to recover to pre-storm levels and thus prevent further erosion in the following days and weeks. However, if the sand eroded from the dunes is swept along the shoreline by longshore drift, and away from the eroded section of dunes, then the next storm event will cause further erosion and retreat of the dune face *(Plate 9)*. If this sand loss is replaced by an influx of sand from offshore or updrift deposits, there may be no nett loss and the dunes should recover over time. Where significant dune erosion persists for several years, it is likely that the sediment balance has been upset resulting in a nett removal of sand from the affected area.

14

Although the sediment balance can be disturbed by natural causes (depletion of the source, a change in the mouth of a river or estuary, gradual shift in wave climate), it is often the result of human activities along an adjacent frontage or nearshore area. These may include dredging, construction of harbour breakwaters, protection of eroding cliffs or construction of beach control structures such as groynes or breakwaters. Erosion in these cases is not natural. An environmentally conscious shoreline manager is faced with the dilemma of accepting erosion of a dune system as a natural process, or implementing management operations that may be destructive to the very habitat and landscape that he seeks to protect.

Regardless of cause, the process of marine erosion of dunes is much more difficult to manage than the deflation described above. It is not generally possible to do anything about the causes of the erosion, namely high tidal levels, winds, rain and wave action, and often not possible to influence the human activities that may exacerbate the situation. The only natural defences that dunes have against the impacts of waves are a wide, high beach in front of them and the binding strength of well developed vegetation. If the beach is undergoing long-term erosion, then it is difficult to remedy this, short of expensive large-scale engineering works such as beach nourishment or the construction of groynes or breakwaters.

In many cases, however, the lowering of beach levels and subsequent rapid erosion of dunes is a short-term problem, that after a few years would naturally "heal" *(Plate 10)*. Indeed the ability of dunes to recover and repair themselves following marine erosion is a major advantage from the viewpoint of long-term shoreline management. Replacing dunes with artificial hard defences such as seawalls may lead to the beach, dunes or structures deteriorating, with potential further expense in repairs and replacement, and should therefore be avoided if at all possible.

The main theme of this Guide, therefore, is to assist in the strengthening and re-building of dunes to reduce the adverse effects of marine erosion, while minimising the risks to people and property behind them. This is largely achieved by palliative measures, designed to reduce the adverse consequences of dune erosion, rather than to try to prevent such erosion entirely.

2.3 Attributes of coastal dunes

Coastal dunes have other important qualities and attributes beyond their role as a natural form of coast protection. These can briefly be summarised as follows:

- Dunes provide a range of important habitats, often with abundant species of flowers, insects and other wildlife *(Plate 11)*. For this reason, many areas of dunes are designated as Sites of Special Scientific Interest or are Local Nature Reserves. Even non-designated dune areas will be locally important havens for wildlife.

Plate 11
Dune systems support distinctive plant communities. The calcareous soils of the machair, especially, encourage the growth of rich and diverse grasslands. N Uist.

- Dunes also have considerable value from the viewpoint of geomorphology, showing how coastal landforms evolve under the action of natural processes (waves, tides and wind) *(Plate 12)*.

Plate 12
Dune systems may be of conservation importance because of the exceptional landforms which they contain. Forvie.

Plate 13
Scotland's golf links are renowned world-wide. Scarista, Harris.

- Many areas of dunes are used for golf courses that are often of considerable commercial and cultural value (*Plate 13*).
- Dunes are popular areas for informal recreation and hence they indirectly generate revenue for the local economy (*Plate 14*).

Plate 14
Dunes are popular areas for informal recreation. St Cyrus.

- Although generally of low agricultural value, dunes are sometimes used for rough grazing, and in some areas form the seaward edge of important lowland areas (particularly the machair in the north west of Scotland) where traditional agriculture continues.
- Some dune areas have also been developed for commercial, industrial and other purposes, with the seaward remnants of the dunes thus becoming even more important as a coastal protection. Examples include chemical works, airfields and military bases.

These various attributes mean that different people and organisations have different perspectives on dune management. When contemplating management activities it is important to bear these views in mind.

2.4 Classification of Scottish dunes

Classification systems can provide a short hand to facilitate discussions, but they are normally either too simple, ignoring subtle differences of type, or too complex and unwieldy. For the purposes of this guide a simple approach is adopted based on processes and regions rather than form.

Dunes on the Western Isles and north west mainland are subject to wet weather, strong westerly winds and very high energy wave conditions. The dunes are fed by calcium rich sands derived from shells and offshore deposits. The resultant dune systems are low, and are often backed by machair *(Plate 15)*. Many of the systems are within small embayments where they are protected from wave induced longshore transport. Dune systems that are in remote or largely undisturbed areas, and systems where public access is effectively managed often enjoy long term stability, with short term erosion balanced by recovery.

Plate 15
Hebridean beach-machair system, Traigh-na-Berie, Lewis

East coast shorelines that are exposed to the North Sea are influenced by westerly winds blowing offshore as well as onshore winds and waves from the north and east. Post-glacial deposits off the present shoreline originally provided a substantial source of sand which was transported onshore by waves as sea levels rose. Opposing onshore and offshore winds result in high foredunes rather than the lower machair systems of the west coast *(Plate 16)*. When sand supplies were plentiful the dunes grew seaward in a series of ridges, but under present conditions the supplies are generally not balancing the losses. The result, in most areas, is long term recession, with this trend underlying short term cycles of erosion and accretion.

Plate 16
Typical east coast beach-dune system with high and extensive foredune ridge, Belhaven.

18

The third major Scottish dune type is found within estuaries *(Plate 17)*. Estuaries are influenced by tidal currents as much as by winds and waves. Dune systems along their shores may be extensive, often fed from intertidal sand banks. However, they can be rapidly destroyed as a result of an unpredictable change in flow patterns and a shift in the distribution of intertidal banks and channels.

Plate 17
Estuarine dune system, St Andrews links, Eden Estuary. Shifting tidal channels can cause dramatic changes on the coast.

Finally, there are a few areas, typically in the outer regions of the Scottish Firths, where dunes are still enjoying a long term trend of accretion as the supply of sand exceeds losses *(Plate 18)*. By definition these frontages are of less interest to this Guide.

Plate 18
Not all dune systems are eroding. At Tentsmuir, lines of anti-tank blocks from the 2nd World War are now situated over 100m from the shore due to ongoing sand accumulation.

As noted earlier, simple classifications do not cover the range of variations. Along the Scottish coast there are numerous dune systems, each with its own specific character. The above classification covers most of them, and can be summarised as:

- smaller embayments suffering occasional severe erosion but relatively stable over the longer term
- extensive open coast systems, subject to short term erosion/accretion cycles, but suffering long term recession
- estuary systems subject to substantial periodic erosion as a result of shifting tidal channels.

3. The legal framework

3.1 Coast Protection Legislation in Scotland

3.1.1 Introduction

A broad range of legislation governs the approval and implementation of coast protection works - that is schemes intended to manage or prevent coastal erosion - and virtually all works outlined in this guide will require certain consents or licences before they can be implemented. The nature of the consents required depends largely upon the precise location of the works relative to high and low water marks, the type and scale of the works and the nature conservation interest of the area concerned.

Table 3.1 provides a detailed breakdown of the consents and approvals typically required of coast protection schemes in Scotland. It should be noted that in the exceptional case of listed buildings or scheduled ancient monuments being affected by the works under consideration, other, additional consents may also need to be sought.

3.1.2 Summary of Legislation

The *Coast Protection Act 1949* (part I) empowers Local Authorities with coastlines (termed 'Coast Protection Authorities' in the Act) to carry out coast protection work inside and outside their area as necessary, subject to the approval of the Scottish Executive[1]. Capital works may, if approved, be eligible for grant aid from the Executive, ranging from 20-80% of eligible costs, depending upon the Authority concerned. Proposed schemes, other than maintenance or emergency operations, must be advertised by the Coast Protection Authority and notice of the works served upon a number of bodies, including SNH and the Scottish Environment Protection Agency (SEPA).

The powers given to the Coast Protection Authorities under the Act are permissive, i.e. Authorities are not obliged to protect eroding coastlines. Instead responsibility for management and prevention of erosion rests with the landowner of the site concerned. Schemes proposed by landowners require the consent of the Coast Protection Authority and are not eligible for grant under the Act. Road, rail and harbour authorities, and certain other bodies with special powers, are exempt from the requirement to gain such consent but must instead give notice to the Coast Protection Authority of any works they propose to carry out.

Further to these requirements, because coast protection works below MHWS might, in theory, affect or interfere with marine transport or navigation, consent is also required for these under part II of the Act from the Scottish Executive Transport Division[2].

The *Food and Environment Protection Act 1985* (FEPA) regulates activities involving construction or deposition of materials upon the seabed. Under FEPA, all operations, including coast protection works, entailing movement of beach sediment or the erection of structures below HWMOST require a licence, in this case from the Scottish Executive Marine Laboratories[3].

Depending upon the nature and scale of the works, most coast protection schemes proposed by individuals or Local Authorities also require planning permission under the *Town and Country Planning (Scotland) Act 1997* (TCPSA), assuming they extend above LWMOST. For major schemes this is the case even where it is the Local Authority itself which proposes the works.

Naturally, the permission of the landowner will need to be sought prior to commencement of works. For foreshore and seabed below HWMOST this will typically be the Crown Estate. Local Authorities retain the power, under the *Coast Protection Act*, to carry out works even where landowner permission is not given. Such schemes, however, require Ministerial approval following consideration of any objections which the landowner may have.

---

[1] *Scottish Executive (Rural Affairs Department), Environment Group, Victoria Quay, Edinburgh. EH6 6QQ.*
[2] *Scottish Executive (Development Department), Transport Division 4, Victoria Quay, Edinburgh. EH6 6QQ.*
[3] *Scottish Executive (Rural Affairs Department), Marine Laboratories, PO Box 101, Aberdeen.*

3.2 Nature Conservation Issues and Legislation

Scotland's coastline is exceptionally important for nature conservation, supporting a wide variety of landforms, rock sequences, habitats and wildlife. The nature conservation interest and landscape of the coastline are safeguarded through a range of natural heritage designations, described in full in *Natural Heritage Designations in Scotland: A Guide* (Scottish Office, December 1998). The most important of these, in terms of beach and dune management, are outlined below.

Around 400 **Sites of Special Scientific Interest** (SSSI) lie wholly or in part along the coastline. Beach-dune systems form a major and integral part of this network. They may be designated as SSSIs because of the plant communities that exist there, the wildlife they support or simply the landforms and geomorphological processes that they exhibit *(Plate 19)*. Coastal erosion and accretion may be integral to these interests; indeed at some sites the erosive processes taking place may actually form part of the designated interest. Conversely, inappropriate coast protection may be damaging to the site's conservation interests.

Plate 19
There are around 400 coastal SSSIs in Scotland, many, like here at Barry Buddon, designated on account of the valuable habitat they provide or dramatic landforms which they exhibit.

Certain of these SSSIs may, in addition, be designated as **Special Areas for Conservation** (SAC). This designation was introduced under the EC Habitats Regulations 1994 and is conferred upon sites considered to be of international importance because of the habitats that exist there. Because of their importance, SACs, along with **Special Protection Areas** (sites of international importance because of the bird populations which they support) are afforded high levels of statutory protection, so as to maintain the nature conservation interests which exist there.

Where planning permission is sought for coast protection works within an SSSI then, under the TCPSA, SNH must be consulted regarding these. Coast protection works are, moreover, listed as a Schedule 2 category development, under the *Environmental Assessment (Scotland) Regulations 1988* (as amended), through which the *EC1985 Directive on Environmental Impact Assessment* is implemented. This means that, in reviewing proposed coast protection works, planning departments are obliged to consider whether or not the works are likely to cause significant environmental effects upon a "sensitive location", such as a SSSI, National Scenic Area (NSA), SAC or SPA (or indeed sites proposed as SACs or SPAs but not yet

designated as such). If so, then the planning authority may require the proponents of the scheme to prepare an environmental assessment of the impact of the works. Such an assessment must also include an outline of the main alternatives considered and the reasons for choosing the preferred option.

In addition to this, should a proposed coast protection scheme be deemed likely to have a significant impact upon a SAC then the EC Habitats Regulations require that an "appropriate assessment" be undertaken by "competent authorities" (typically relevant Government Departments and the Local Authority). Guidance on the nature of the assessment is provided in the relevant legislation. Similar procedures apply to SPAs.

Table 3.1 Coast Protection Works - Requirements For Consents And Consultations

(Prepared by D Tyldesley Associates for SNH).

Construction, Alteration or Improvement Works for the Protection of land against Erosion and Encroachment by the Sea. Key: CPA = Coast Protection Act 1949; CPAu = Coast Protection Authority; EA = Environmental Assessment; FEPA = Food and Environment Protection Act 1985; OLD = Operation Likely to Damage; PA = Planning Authority; P Dev = Permitted Development; SERAD = Scottish Executive Rural Affairs Department; SEDD = Scottish Executive Development Department (Transport Division); TCPSA = Town and Country Planning (Scotland) Act, 1997; WCA = Wildlife and Countryside Act 1981.

Proposer	Administrative Locality	Location of Works	CPA Pt1 SERAD Consent	CPA Pt1 CPAu Consent	CPA Pt2 SEDD Consent	FEPA SERAD Consent	Scale	TCPSA	EA Regulations 1988 / 1994	Habitats Regulations 1994	WCA S.28
Coast Protection Authority	Within its own area	Those works above MHWS	Requires consent	Not required if proposed by CPAu in its own area	Not required	Not required	>£100,000	Full planning permission required	If significant environmental effects ES required with full planning application, cannot be P Dev	If significant effect on a Natura 2000 site PA and SERAD must undertake appropriate assessment	OLD notice not required
		Those works above MHWS					<£100,000 or <200 cubic metres and <4m high	Permitted development	P Dev if no significant environmental effects	Permitted development if no adverse effect on the integrity of a Natura 2000 site	OLD notice required if on SSSI
		Works between MHWS and MLWS	Requires consent	Not required if proposed by CPAu in its own area	Required if likely to endanger navigation	Requires consent	>£100,000	Full planning permission required	If significant environmental effects ES and full planning application required cannot be P Dev	If significant effect on a Natura 2000 site PA and SERAD must undertake appropriate assessment	OLD notice not required
		Works between MHWS and MLWS					<£100,000 or <200 cubic metres and <4m high	Permitted development	P Dev if no significant environmental effects	Permitted development if no adverse effect on the integrity of a Natura 2000 site	OLD notice required if on SSSI
		Works below MLWS	Requires consent	Not required if proposed by CPAu in its own area	Required if likely to endanger navigation	Requires consent	Any scale	Not applicable	If significant environmental effects ES required with FEPA and CPA Pt1 applications	If significant effect on a Natura 2000 site SERAD should undertake appropriate assessment	OLD notice only required if SSSI below MLWS
Coast Protection Authority	Outwith the area of the CPAu	Those works above MHWS	Requires consent	Requires 28 days notice to the other CPAu	Not required	Not required	Any scale	Requires full planning application to be made to the other PA	If significant environmental effects ES required with full planning application	If significant effect on a Natura 2000 site other PA and SERAD must undertake appropriate assessment	OLD notice not required
		Works between MHWS and MLWS	Requires consent	Requires 28 days notice to the other CPAu	Required if likely to obstruct or endanger navigation	Requires consent	Any scale	Requires full planning application to be made to the other PA	If significant effects ES required with full planning and FEPA application	If significant effect on a Natura 2000 site other PA and SERAD must undertake appropriate assessment	OLD notice not required
		Works below MLWS	Requires consent	Requires 28 days notice to the other CPAu	Required if likely to obstruct or endanger	Requires consent	Any scale	Not applicable	If significant effects ES required with FEPA application	If significant effect on a Natura 2000 site SERAD should undertake appropriate assessment	OLD notice only required if SSSI below MLWS

Activity	Works	Order approval (First Minister)	Notice / consent to CPAu	FEPA / navigation licence	Coast protection consent	Scale	Development	EIA (ES)	Natura 2000 appropriate assessment	OLD notice
Roads Authority — Works required for or incidental to the maintenance or improvement of a road	Those works above MHWS	Not required	Requires 28 days notice to the CPAu	Required if likely to obstruct or endanger navigation	Requires consent	Any scale within or adjoining the boundaries of a road	Permitted development	If significant effects ES required with full planning application	If significant effect on a Natura 2000 site must submit application to PA for approval, PA must undertake an appropriate assessment	If permitted development OLD notice required
	Works between MHWS and MLWS	Not required	Requires 28 days notice to the CPAu	Required if likely to obstruct or endanger navigation	Requires consent	Any scale within or adjoining the boundaries of a road	Not applicable	If significant effects ES required with FEPA application	If significant effect on a Natura 2000 site SERAD should undertake appropriate assessment	OLD notice only required if SSSI below MLWS
	Works below MLWS	Not required	Requires 28 days notice to the CPAu	Not required	Not required	Any scale	Not applicable	If significant effects ES required with FEPA application	If significant effect on a Natura 2000 site SERAD should undertake appropriate assessment	OLD notice not required
Private Landowner under Coast Protection Act a private coast protection scheme	Those works above MHWS	Order must be approved by First Minister	Consent of CPAu required	Not required	Not required	Any scale	Full planning permission required	If significant effects ES required with full planning application	If significant effect on a Natura 2000 site PA and SERAD should undertake appropriate assessment	OLD notice not required
	Works between MHWS and MLWS	Not required	Consent of CPAu required	If likely to obstruct or endanger navigation	Consent required	Any scale	Full planning permission required	If significant effects ES required with full planning application	If significant effect on a Natura 2000 site PA and SERAD should undertake appropriate assessment	OLD notice only required if SSSI below MLWS
	Works below MLWS	Not required	Consent of CPAu required	If likely to obstruct or endanger navigation	Consent required	Any scale	N/A	If significant effects ES required with FEPA application	If significant effect on a Natura 2000 site SERAD should undertake appropriate assessment	No OLD notice required
Private Landowner under Land Drainage (Scotland) Act 1958 an improvement order to combat erosion	Those works above MHWS	Order must be approved by First Minister	Not required	Not required	Not required	Any scale	Normally a deemed planning permission or P Dev but see next column	If significant effects ES required with full planning and order and FEPA application	P Dev if no adverse effect on integrity of Natura 2000 Site	OLD notice required
	Works between MHWS and MLWS	Order must be approved by First Minister	Not required	Required if likely to obstruct or endanger navigation	Consent required	Any scale	Normally a deemed planning permission or P Dev but see next column	P Dev if no significant effects	P Dev if no adverse effect on integrity of Natura 2000 Site	No OLD notice required
	Works below MLWS	Order must be approved by First Minister	Not required	Required if likely to obstruct or endanger navigation	Consent required	Any scale	N/A	If significant effects ES required with order and FEPA application	If significant effect on a Natura 2000 site SERAD should undertake appropriate assessment	OLD notice only required if SSSI below MLWS

4. Strategic approach to dune management

Managing marine erosion of dunes requires an understanding of the physical and ecological processes active both at the site and in the wider coastal environment, an understanding of the risks to the human and natural environment, an understanding of the effectiveness and consequences of the possible management decisions and a clear understanding of the short and longer term management objectives for the site. All shoreline sites are part of larger coastal systems. Waves and currents active on a section of beach are often generated by forces that are remote from the site. The sediment that makes up the beach is often derived from a source that is both temporally and physically distant. As a result, management operations can have unforeseen impacts locally or even on sites many miles away, either immediately or, potentially, years later.

4.1 Processes

Every site is influenced by physical processes that cause erosion and recovery of the dunes. These include winds, waves, water levels and currents that drive cross-shore and longshore sediment transport. In turn these processes are influenced by topography, bathymetry, geomorphology, river flows, coastal structures and dredging operations. Dunes are also influenced by rainfall, temperature, sediment chemistry and natural grazing as these factors affect the type and health of the vegetation. There are numerous publications that discuss these processes in general terms (for example, Ranwell and Boar, 1986), but a shoreline manager should also be aware of how these processes work at the site of interest.

A good starting point for developing an understanding of the shoreline is the geomorphological and recent history. Information on the coastal and nearshore surface and drift geology is available from British Geological Survey publications and maps. Recent evolution can be derived from analysis of historic map series, charts, aerial photographs, surveys and engineering records. Important sources of regional information are provided by the Coastal Cells series (HR Wallingford, 2000) and the Beaches of Scotland series (Countryside Commission for Scotland, 1969-1981), both of which are fully referenced in Section 6.1 and Figures 6.1 and 6.2. The former series of 11 reports was commissioned in 1996 by SNH, SOAEFD (now SERAD) and Historic Scotland to provide a broad understanding of the character and processes of the coastal regime around the Scottish coast. The latter series of 19 reports provide a detailed description of every sandy beach and dune system in Scotland including morphology, land use, management pressures and the nature and extent of coastal erosion; although some information is now dated, this series is of considerable value to coastal managers. Recent information is also available for some areas where Shoreline Management Plans and analogous studies have been completed (Section 6.1, Figure 6.2) *(Plate 20)*.

Plate 20
A series of erosion concerns, such as here at Dysart, has prompted Fife Council to prepare a Shoreline Management Plan for its entire coastline.

Useful information can also be derived from discussions with local residents and beach users, and from more formal consultation with other interest groups (Section 4.4). The resulting picture may be one of long term erosion, accretion or stability, combined with short term cycles of rapid erosion and recovery. Care should be taken if the data set is skewed to the very recent past and is dominated by records of erosion; such information may be atypical of the long term situation, and may lead to a hasty decision to undertake unnecessary works.

Reasons for the evolution may be an obvious change in local shoreline processes caused by specific human activities, such as the construction of a harbour, the dredging of a channel or an increase in recreational use of the dunes. Less obvious may be the effects of medium term (1-20 years) changes in weather patterns, tidal cycles (up to 19 years) or a gradual reduction in sediment supply from a natural source.

Met Office data may reveal reasons for changes to dune stability. Unusually severe storms over Spring tide periods may have caused rapid erosion, while a sustained shift in the dominant wind directions may have caused change to the longshore drift direction, causing erosion in one area and accretion elsewhere. Alternatively, a drop in average wind speeds may have reduced the aeolian transport of sand that feeds the dune face, or a prolonged dry spell may have reduced the vigour of foredune vegetation and restricted dune recovery.

The causes of erosion within an estuary may be difficult to understand. Shoreline evolution is often linked to the ever changing distribution of channels and banks. These features are influenced by local wind waves, waves entering through the estuary mouth, ebb and flood tide currents and fresh water flows, as well as human activities such as dredging, reclamation and the construction of training walls or navigation facilities. Prediction of evolution will require the services of a specialist estuary consultant.

Having established the background to the site evolution, and prior to committing any significant effort to erosion control, it is advisable to establish a monitoring programme. The objective of monitoring would be to expand the desk based knowledge of the processes active at the site and to develop a first hand understanding of the extent of the erosion problem. Minor shoreline works might be undertaken during the monitoring period, but the implementation of any major schemes should be delayed until the managers have confidence in their understanding of the site and the potential consequences of their actions. Monitoring approaches are outlined in Appendix 2.

4.2 Risks

Having considered whether erosion is a short term fluctuation or an ongoing problem, and whether the affected area is localised or widespread, the manager must consider what assets may be at risk and over what timescales losses may occur. These assets may be natural, such as a rare habitat or unusual landform, or they may be human, ranging from a footpath to a major residential or industrial development. Protection of natural assets is contentious, as erosion is a natural process and management operations may be more damaging than the erosion itself.

The risk to human assets must be balanced against many considerations, including the inevitable damage to the environment. At one end of the risk scale it may be considered better or more cost effective to lose or move an asset rather than invest effort and money into erosion management operations. At the other end it may well be obvious that further erosion is totally unacceptable and that the costs and consequences of defences are fully justified *(Plate 23)*.

25

Plate 21
If there is a long term erosion trend, hard defences on dunes may need to be extended in due course to avoid outflanking. At Ruby Bay, Elie, defences have been extended at least six times.

Attempts to interfere with natural processes within any dynamic natural environment can lead to the creation of more problems than are solved. Beach-dune management can often be seen as successful at a local level, with the risk to backshore assets being reduced. However this success may either be short term or it may be achieved at the cost of damage to adjacent areas. If shoreline erosion is both long term and widespread, schemes to protect the dunes will face ever increasing attack from waves and currents as the foreshore continues to recede *(Plate 21)*. Alternatively, if erosion is cyclical and there is a reasonable expectation of natural recovery, expenditure on schemes may well be wasted.

Management of dunes within a small embayment can often be undertaken without consideration of a wider area, as sediment transport processes may well be restricted to the limits of the bay. Where the dunes are within an estuary or along a stretch of open coast the impacts of operations can be more widespread. In these situations, common along much of the Scottish east and south west coasts, managers must be aware that the defence of one section of shoreline may result in accelerated erosion elsewhere.

From an understanding of the coastal processes the manager can make an informed prediction of the risks and costs associated with allowing coastal processes to proceed unhindered. If these risks and costs are considered unacceptable, or at least undesirable, consideration must turn to the effectiveness, costs, consequences and sustainability of possible management operations.

4.3 Funding

This Guide does not cover funding arrangements for coastal works. However, before plans for management are pursued beyond the preliminary appraisal stage potential funding sources should be established; typical costs are discussed in Section 5 and Appendix 1. Consideration should be given to both initial capital costs and to on-going management. The latter may be of particular importance to schemes that are considered to have a lower environmental impact, such as vegetation transplanting, fencing or beach recycling. Ongoing funding should be set aside for all management operations to cover the costs of future monitoring of beach levels and dune face evolution.

4.4 Consultation

There are a variety of parties with interests in the coastal zone, all of whom may wish to have a say in the management of dune erosion. Some are Statutory Consultees who must be approached prior to scheme implementation (Section 3), while others can be consulted voluntarily. Identification of those relevant to a specific site, followed by consultation, may lead to a better understanding of the processes ad risks as well as to a consensus view on the most appropriate management actions. Potential consultees include:

- Foreshore owners (Unitary Authority, Crown Estate, National Trust, private estate, harbour authority, etc.)
- Scottish Natural Heritage
- Scottish Environment Protection Agency
- Adjacent landowners (Unitary Authority, private landowner, nature trust, MoD, etc.)
- Land managers where different from land owners
- Historic Scotland
- RSPB
- Tourist Boards
- Fishing associations, nature trusts, recreational groups, etc.

Each of these consultees may have a different perception of the value of the beach-dune system and therefore see erosion management as serving a different purpose. By bringing them together and explaining the background issues and the potential solutions a useful consensus may be built. Undertaking voluntary consultation early in the planning stage may well avoid later conflicts with Statutory Consultees or, in extreme cases, the costs of Public Enquiries. Where public funding of a scheme is not available, consultation may lead to opportunities to share costs or obtain other management resources (volunteer labour, materials, access rights). Figure 5.1 presents a flow diagram of the management process, putting the various phases into a logical sequence.

4.5 Coastal cells and Shoreline management plans

In recent years, Shoreline Management Plans (SMPs) have been advocated as potentially useful documents for establishing sustainable coastal defence policies for specific lengths of coastline. Routinely these are based on natural divisions of the coastline, called coastal cells. The benefits of this strategic approach to erosion management are explained in detail in the SNH report *The Potential Application of Shoreline Management Planning to Scotland* (J Hansom et al., 1999). In addressing erosion on specific dune systems, the coastal manager should ensure that their management proposals are in keeping with any SMP which may exist for that area (see Figure 6.2).

5. Management options

5.1 Possible approaches

The earlier sections of this Guide have looked at the processes and risks related to beach-dune systems, and have pointed towards the need to treat each site as a unique situation; generic dune management approaches are not appropriate. This Chapter sets out the underlying issues involved in selecting a management approach that will achieve the specific objectives established for each site.

It is assumed throughout this section that all sites being considered have assets at risk from erosion and that protection of these assets will be balanced against impacts on the environment. Most approaches to erosion management are damaging to the environment to a greater or lesser extent. This is particularly so for projects entailing civil engineering operations such as revetment and sea-wall construction or major beach renourishment schemes. The inclusion of such approaches herein does not, therefore, indicate approval or commendation of them from SNH in all circumstances. Rather, they are included to provide a comprehensive guide to the options available to coastal managers and to promote good practice, from an environmental perspective, in the design and implementation of coastal defences, whatever approach is adopted.

Questions to be answered include:

- What are the objectives?
- Will the scheme achieve the objectives?
- Over what time scale will it be effective?
- What will be the impacts on the natural environment and the landscape over different timescales?
- Are the resources (materials, equipment, labour, funding) available for both initial implementation and long term maintenance?
- Are the short and long term costs justified by the benefits?
- What will be the impacts on adjacent areas?
- Are there more appropriate options?

There are four general approaches to managing dune erosion:

- Non-interference, allowing natural processes to continue while accepting losses or taking appropriate action to relocate any backshore assets at risk.
- Delay erosion using small scale, short term (5-10 year life) schemes that can be implemented at relatively low cost and that will have a minimum impact on the coastal environment.
- Defend the frontage selectively using methods that may require the involvement of specialist consultants and may have a high impact on the immediate environment and coastal landscape; these may be short term, but are more likely to have a longer life expectancy (5-30 year life).
- Establish a fixed shoreline using large scale, long term (20-50 year life) defences that will require the involvement of specialist consultants and will significantly alter the coastal environment, landscape and recreational use of the beach.

There is obviously some overlap between these approaches and some differences of opinion as to what may be short term or long term, and what their impact on the environment may be. Schemes that have a life expectancy (without maintenance) of up to 10 years are considered short term in relation to the natural environment. In addition it should be noted that these approaches are not independent – indeed it may well be advantageous to combine small scale, short term management with engineered schemes to encourage dune systems to redevelop after being damaged.

Selection of the appropriate approach, or combination of approaches depends on the objectives and constraints relevant to the site. Scheme options suitable to each approach are set out in a series of Summaries presented in Appendix 1. These include:

Non-interference	● Adaptive management
Small scale, short term	● Dune grass planting
	● Dune thatching
	● Dune fencing
	● Beach re-cycling
	● Sand bag structures
	● Beach nourishment
	● Beach drainage
	● Gabion structures (see note below)
Selective frontages	● Rock or gabion headlands
	● Groynes
	● Nearshore breakwaters
	● Artificial reefs
Large scale, long term	● Rock revetments
	● Timber revetments and breastwork
	● Impermeable revetments and seawalls

(Note. Gabions are often associated with poor shoreline management practice, and should only be used in specific circumstances. If they are regularly exposed to wave attack then they will have a short life before becoming ineffective and an eyesore. However, used as a buried defence or within sheltered areas of an estuary they can be both effective and unobtrusive. Their position in the short-term, small scale category is debatable as they can be used over long frontages, and if well maintained can last for longer than 10 years before needing substantial renovation.)

The Summaries set out sufficient information about each option for the reader to make an informed decision about their appropriate use. The Summaries of small scale, short term operations provide information that will allow implementation, possibly using volunteer or unskilled labour. It is assumed that larger schemes will only be put in place following preliminary appraisal and design studies by a competent coastal consultant; the relevant Summaries present information to allow the proposed designs to be assessed for appropriateness and potential long term impacts.

Appendix 1 also includes a summary of "novel" methods, providing a brief indication of the reasons for not giving them serious consideration.

5.2 Engineering considerations

There are a number of engineering issues that need to be considered prior to selection of an appropriate approach and option. These include:

● availability and life expectancy of materials
● transport and placement methods
● costs
● environmental impacts
● work windows
● long term maintenance

5.2.1 Materials

Dune management may require anything from marram glass transplants and brushwood up to 6 tonne armour stone and reinforced concrete. Availability, applications and costs will vary depending on location, and may dictate the viability of a scheme. Other considerations governing choice of materials will be appearance, environmental impact, life expectancy and public safety.

Vegetation transplanting, thatching and fencing may well be considered as a part of any scheme, no matter how small or large. Transplants for a small scheme over tens of metres may well be available at no cost from the local dune system, but schemes covering longer lengths of shoreline will probably need a commercial supply or the development of a managed nursery. Either way, supplies will be limited and work will have to be planned well in advance. Fencing or thatching supplies should be readily available at any location. Chestnut palings or synthetic fabrics can be purchased and delivered to any site in the required quantities, though transport costs to islands may be high. Thatching materials, such as brush wood or forestry waste, are often available for the cost of transport, but supplies may be limited on exposed west and north coast sites. These materials have a life expectancy of less than 5 years and are likely to need regular maintenance to retain effectiveness, an acceptable appearance and minimal hazard to beach users.

Sediment for re-cycling or nourishment can be a problem. Re-cycling involves moving material from a point of accretion to a point of erosion within a local process area. The accretion point may be further along the shoreline, for example next to a breakwater or at an estuary mouth, or it may be down the beach face at a low tide bar. Prior to any detailed consideration of hydraulic or ecological issues, the ownership and licensing arrangements for re-cycling must be established. Much of the Scottish foreshore up to HWMOST belongs to the Crown Estate, but other owners include Unitary Councils, private estates and the National Trust. The beach above HWMOST normally belongs with the adjoining backshore property. Movement of sediment across any ownership boundaries may lead to conflicts unless early consultation has established a consensus. Before implementation appropriate legal consents (Chapter 3) will have to be sought.

Wherever the source of the re-cycled sediment it is critical to establish whether removal will create a new erosion problem or whether the impact will be negligible. It is also important to establish that the source material is compatible with the erosion area in terms of hydraulic response, impact on the ecosystem and impact on recreation. Annual, or even post-storm, re-cycling may be required to provide on going protection.

Beach nourishment uses material imported from outside the local coastal process unit. Sources may be quarries, licensed dredging areas or spoil taken from navigation dredging *(Plate 22)*. Quarried sand or gravel is often appropriate for smaller schemes that are close to the quarry or have very easy road access. Larger schemes normally rely on dredged material transported by sea and pumped ashore via floating pipelines or directly from the vessel to the beach. Licensed dredging areas are limited to a few estuary sites around Scotland and schemes will be competing with the aggregate industry for both sediment and delivery vessels. In some locations material may be available from dredged harbours and navigation channels, but this source is less reliable in terms of available quantities, material grading and quality. High proportions of potentially contaminated muds may render this source inappropriate, especially if dredged from estuarine locations. As with re-cycling, nourishment is likely to need regular top ups to maintain effectiveness as a dune protection measure, making long term management costs higher than might be expected.

Plate 22
Sand for a recent beach renourishment scheme at Montrose was obtained by re-using uncontaminated maintenance dredgings from the adjacent South Esk channel instead of dumping these at sea.

Sand bag structures normally make use of sturdy geotextile bags, filled on site using local sand. In most cases both the bags and sand are easily available. As the bags are liable to damage, both from natural causes and vandalism, structures are best buried with re-cycled sand, only to be exposed during extreme storms when they will act as a final line of defence. Damaged bags will release the enclosed sand harmlessly back to the beach, leaving only the geotextile to be retrieved. Structures are likely to have a life of only about 10 years.

Rock filled gabion baskets have frequently been used for coastal defence, and have earned a poor reputation. Gabions have been known to fail when used in unsuitable locations, placed and filled with insufficient attention to recommended construction practices, or when managers have not attended to proper maintenance. Damaged baskets release cobbles or quarried rock onto the beach, and the baskets themselves become a hazardous eye-sore of rusting wire. However, when designed, built and maintained correctly gabions can provide good service with minimal ecological or visual impact. Life expectancy before a major rebuild can be as much as 20 years, though 10 years is more likely. Gabions will last longer, have less environmental impact and be less intrusive on the coastal landscape if they are buried into the dune face, only reappearing during severe erosion events. Under accreting conditions gabions can be buried by wind blown sand, and will allow dune vegetation to be re-established. On open coasts, gabions may only be appropriate as sloping revetments. In estuaries, where wave attack will be less severe, they can also be used to form other structures such as groynes. Baskets and appropriate rock are easily obtained for most sites.

Rock, from small boulders to large armour stone can be used effectively in erosion protection schemes. Established design guidance is available to ensure that rock structures are built to give optimum performance and cost (CIRIA/CUR, 1991). Structures may include headlands, revetments, breakwaters, reefs or groynes. The required rock sizes will vary according to structure function, wave conditions, water levels, structure slopes, permeability and acceptable damage criteria. Rock has the advantage of durability and flexibility, meaning that structures can suffer some damage without failing and can be rebuilt or even removed if necessary. As with gabions, rock revetments can be buried to reduce their visual impact under normal conditions, but may be re-exposed during storms. In Scotland, good quality rock is generally available and will have an effectively unlimited life.

Timber structures are less popular today than in the past. Softwood only lasts a few years in the harsh and abrasive marine environment. Hardwood lasts longer, but is expensive and should only be sourced from acceptably managed forests. However, timber is a flexible building material, and can be used to form solid or permeable revetments, vertical breastwork and groynes. A 20-30 year life would be considered successful. Impermeable structures built in areas subject to regular wave activity may suffer from localised toe scour that may cause structural failure.

Solid revetments and seawalls are not normally considered appropriate for dune protection, but can be built from asphalt, blockwork, pre-cast concrete units or in situ concrete. These materials are readily available in urban areas but are costly to transport to remote locations. Structures can be designed to enhance public access to the foreshore and can accommodate promenades and seafront roads, but they normally disrupt the natural dynamism of dune systems and replace it with an artificial shoreline. Construction costs are very high and the services of civil engineering consultants are required. Assuming no major hydraulic failure these structures should have a design life of up to 50 years.

Other materials seen along the shoreline include building rubble, broken concrete slabs, re-cycled tyres, patented mattresses of linked concrete blocks, re-cycled construction materials such as concrete pipes, slag, etc. Apart from the block mattresses, the costs of these materials are very low, as are the aesthetic qualities. If the dumped materials are sufficiently large and robust (such as broken concrete slabs) then they may provide a long lasting defence. More often the materials are unable to withstand wave attack and break down rapidly to be spread across the beach. Patented concrete block mattresses are not low cost, but suffer equally from rapid damage as they are easily undermined or lifted by hydraulic forces.

5.2.2 Transport and placement

A significant proportion of the costs for most coast protection materials is in the transport and placement. Work on dune systems can impose additional costs due to concerns over destruction of landforms and habitats, and the problems of working in remote locations. Delivery from the sea of bulk materials (rock or beach sediment) is often preferred as backshore damage is minimised, although land access will still have to be provided for plant, labour and additional materials.

Haul roads will have to be built across the dunes unless access can be provided from an existing route along the shoreline. Delivery from the sea avoids these problems, but will suffer from nearshore navigation hazards, weather downtime and tidal restrictions.

5.2.3 Costs

The costs of dune erosion management can vary from almost nothing to several million pounds per kilometre. Major cost elements are labour and materials for initial works, with secondary elements being preliminary investigations, consultant's fees, pre- and post-project monitoring, site equipment, site access, permissions and ongoing maintenance.

Small dune grass transplanting or thatching schemes can be undertaken by unskilled volunteer labour using locally available materials. As the consequences of inappropriate implementation are minimal, there would be no need to undertake significant preliminary investigations, involve consultants or establish any rigorous monitoring programmes. Costs would be very low, but the life of the scheme may be short and the benefits very localised.

Larger schemes involving the transport and placement of rock and / or imported beach material, possibly combined with transplanting, fencing and recreational management will need the services of specialists. Preliminary investigations, benefit cost studies, site monitoring, legal procedures, tender preparation and long term management planning will all need the attention of a competent coastal consultant. Contractors will need to source and transport materials, provide acceptable site access routes for heavy plant, ensure site safety for staff and the public, and make good any damage to the environment.

5.2.4   Environmental impacts

Erosion management operations may have unwanted impacts on the ecology, geomorphology and appearance of a dune system. Decisions on the most appropriate management approach at a given site should be driven in part by the desire to minimise these impacts so as to preserve the natural characteristics of the dunes. It is important to bear in mind that erosion of dunes is a natural process and should not normally be regarded as a problem. Problems only arise when erosion threatens human activities or assets, or when the erosion is the result of human interference with coastal processes along an adjacent frontage.

All human activity within a dune system will cause some damage. Simply walking over the dunes to reach the beach will damage the vegetation, and repeated use of an uncontrolled track may well result in a blow out through the yellow dunes. Moving machinery through the dunes will cause much greater damage, through direct destruction of vegetation, disturbance of previously stable sand and compaction of soils. Dune slacks are equally susceptible to damage as the dunes themselves. Heavy machinery working in the intertidal area, particularly in estuaries, will also damage benthic communities, although these are generally quick to recover.

Dune grass planting and thatching are generally seen as beneficial, but care should be taken not to introduce non-indigenous seeds or shoots that may change the composition of the dune flora; sea buckthorn (*Hippophae rhamnoides*) is particularly invasive when used for thatching. Fencing is also seen as generally beneficial, but lack of planning for suitable public access may encourage people to make their own routes through the dunes, while lack of maintenance may leave derelict fences as an eyesore on the coastal landscape.

Construction of continuous defences along an eroding dune face will dramatically change the coastal landscape and will disrupt the natural interchange of sand between beach and dune *(Plate 24)*. This should be avoided if at all possible as the impacts are effectively irreversible. Seawalls and large revetments generally allow some wind blown sand to reach the dunes, but prevent the return of sand to the beach during storm erosion events. The reduced amounts of blown sand prevent grasses like marram from thriving, and the natural succession of dune habitats from unstable foredunes, through marram dominated yellow dunes to stable grey dunes and machair tends to break down to a simple jump from upper beach to stable backshore vegetation. Interspersing lengths of protection with open dune faces retains at least some of the natural succession and allows natural cycles of erosion or accretion to continue. Wherever possible any form of continuous hard structure should be placed as a final line of defence along the backshore rather than within the active foreshore. With the exception of artificial reef breakwaters all forms of discontinuous hard structures should also be built high on the beach and certainly above HWMOST.

Plate 24

'Hard' structures of rock or concrete may offer greater medium term security than most other defences but have a strong landscape impact and obscure or destroy backshore habitats and landforms. Impacts are effectively irreversible.

Increasing the width and elevation of the upper beach and dune face by recycling or nourishment is an attractive option for erosion management, but has environmental drawbacks. The physical and chemical properties of the new material should be consistent with the existing beach and dunes *(Plate 22)*. Coarser material (shingle) may be more stable than sand, but will increase the slope of the upper beach and change the appearance of the shoreline. Finer material (silt) mixed in with imported sand will tend to be taken into suspension by wave action and removed from the beach; the increased suspended load can be damaging to nearshore fisheries and benthic communities. Sediment with a different chemical composition (e.g. acidity) or from a heavily polluted source (e.g. dredged from a port channel) may have an adverse effect on dune vegetation. Dumping and spreading of the new material may well damage the existing intertidal and dune face communities by smothering or by compaction under the wheels of heavy earth moving plant. Any large schemes involving recycling or nourishment should be preceded by an environmental impact assessment to establish the significance of these impacts on the local site.

Finally, consideration should be given to the full life environmental impacts of proposed management operations. The manager must consider not only the local short term impact of a scheme, but also:

- the impact on the source area for materials (offshore dredging areas, rock quarry, forests, etc)
- the impact of transport to the site (road congestion and surface damage, noise levels, risk of accidents at sea or on roads, access through dunes, etc)
- trapping of seaweed and other debris along the upper beach (visual impact, smell, flies and rodents, health hazard, etc)
- the impact of damaged or life expired materials on the shoreline (synthetic fencing materials, geotextile sand bags, gabion baskets and rock fill, timber, concrete, rock, etc).
- the long term evolution of the beach and dunes and the effectiveness of structures over their full life.

Management plans should allow for these environmental impacts during the decision process, particularly where costs are being passed on to future generations. Mitigation measures and good working practices to minimise impacts should be built in to designs, agreed with contractors and monitored rigorously during initial and ongoing operations.

5.2.5 Work windows

Coastal works are affected by limited work windows. Seasonal conditions often restrict work to the spring and autumn: in winter the weather may be too harsh and the days too short, while in summer work may disrupt recreational use of the beach. Daily tidal cycles will restrict work below the high tide line and access along the beach, although dune face work may be largely unaffected. Other restrictions may be imposed by natural events such as bird nesting or migration, or by optimum seasons for vegetation transplanting or dune recovery. Each site will have its own set of restrictions, and these may well influence decisions on the initial scheme or the long term management options.

5.2.6   Maintenance

Short term works such as transplanting, fencing, re-cycling, sand bagging and even gabion placement will need a defined maintenance and replacement programme as part of the preliminary scheme appraisal. Post-storm, seasonal or annual inspections will be required, followed by appropriate maintenance and repair work. This commitment must be costed and programmed from the outset if erosion is to be managed effectively.

Other more substantial schemes may require a much lower level of long term commitment, but will have to be monitored to ensure ongoing effectiveness. At many sites foreshore erosion will be an ongoing process and may cause local scour or general beach level reduction, resulting in structural instability. Solid defences may need to have toe aprons added to prevent undermining, while gabions may deform to the point of basket failure. Rock structures are unlikely to collapse, but may need some re-shaping or extension to maintain the expected standard of defence. Monitoring may also reveal outflanking problems as the dune face at the end of a structure suffers ongoing erosion, requiring lateral extensions to retain effectiveness. The economic and environmental costs of these future works must be allowed for during the selection and planning stage of scheme development. Failure to do so may place an unacceptable burden on future generations and result in the loss of important environmental assets.

5.3 Recommended approaches

The underlying principles of shoreline management are to match the solution to the problem and to minimise the disruption to natural processes. Ideally dune systems would be left free from backshore development, and therefore erosion management would not be required. This principle should be fundamental to the planning guidelines for all coastal authorities. All soft shorelines should be considered as potentially erodable, even if they appear stable at present, and competent guidance should be sought as to an appropriate set back distance for any new coastal development. Unfortunately, even the most remote Scottish beaches are often already affected by some form of human development. Typically backshore recreational assets, such as caravan parks, footpaths or golf courses, are threatened by erosion, whether seasonal or long term. In extreme cases the threatened backshore assets may also include housing or industrial facilities.

Management responses to the threat of asset loss should start with consideration of adapting the backshore to allow natural erosion to continue. In many cases this will be the only practical solution, as erosion may be an irreversible trend, and the long-term cost of defences may be greater than the value of the property at risk. This approach may be coupled with small scale, short term works to delay the onset of asset loss, or with selective defences to protect the most important assets while accepting the loss of others. If erosion continues and further losses are considered unacceptable then the level of response may have to escalate to large scale works.

Figure 5.1 presents a flow diagram to assist the shoreline manager in moving from an observation of erosion to the implementation of a management plan. This process is strongly linked to monitoring, which is discussed further in Appendix 2.

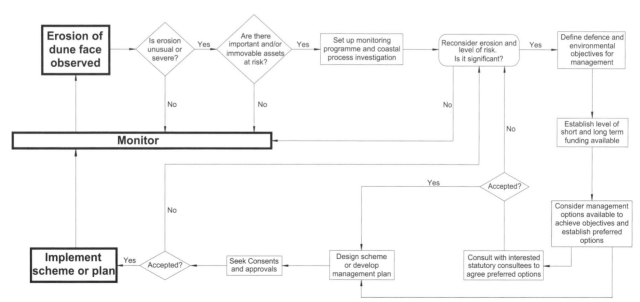

Figure 5.1   Dune management planning and implementation flow diagram

Table 5.1 summarises potential responses to different generalised risk situations based on the nature of the assets at risk. The selection of specific approaches will depend on the characteristics of the site. Other factors such as coastal processes, site access, availability of materials and labour, acceptability of a commitment to long term management, recreational use of the area, financial resources and the conservation interests of the site will also play a part in the decision process.

Table 5.2 provides a further multi-criteria guide to assist in the selection of management options. Each approach is graded for initial and long term maintenance cost, life expectancy of benefits assuming no maintenance and impact on habitat, landform, landscape and coastal processes. The star system is indicative only, as every case must be considered independently. The ideal scheme will provide the asset protection required while minimising costs and impacts and maximising life expectancy.

Table 5.1 Selection of shoreline management options for beach/ dune systems based on assets at risk

NB This table is indicative only. Selection of the specific approach to adopt will depend also on factors such as coastal processes, site access, availability of materials and labour, acceptability of a commitment to long term management, recreational use of the area, financial resources and the conservation interests of the site.

Assets at risk	Open Coast		Estuaries	
	Approaches	Indicative costs per 100m length	Approaches	Indicative costs per 100m length
Coastal habitats and landforms	Non-intervention or minor works to enhance sand retention (i.e. fencing, planting, thatching)	£0 - £10,000	As Open Coast	£0 - £10,000
Low economic value or short residual life (<5 years) (e.g. grazing land, amenity areas, golf rough and fairways, military exercise areas, etc)	Abandon or replace assets elsewhere (Adaptive Management), plus minor works to delay losses (i.e. fencing, planting, thatching)	£0 - £10,000	As Open Coast. If backshore flood risk area is extensive, inland embankments may be required.	£0 - £10,000
Mobile or replaceable (e.g. caravans, golf tees/ green, car parks, amenity buildings, etc)	Move or rebuild assets inland (Adaptive Management), plus minor works to delay onset of move (i.e. fencing, planting, thatching, beach re-cycling, sand bag or gabion revetments)	£0 - £30,000	As Open Coast. If backshore flood risk area is extensive inland embankments may be required.	£0 - £20,000
Discrete assets of moderate to high value and medium to long residual life (>5 years)	Adaptive Management for main frontage, plus: • Rock or gabion headlands, • Nearshore breakwaters, • Artificial reefs, plus minor works to delay erosion between structures (i.e. fencing, planting, thatching, beach re-cycling, gabion revetments)	£20,000 - £100,000	• Rock or gabion headlands • Groynes to deflect flows • Plus minor works to delay erosion between structures (i.e. fencing, planting, thatching, beach re-cycling, sand bag or gabion revetments) • May also require backshore flood embankments if unprotected assets are on low ground	£10,000 - £50,000
Moderate economic value or medium residual life (5-25 years) (Low density housing, roads, large caravan sites, military installations, etc)	• Series of nearshore breakwaters • Rock groynes (on mixed sediment beaches where littoral drift is active and downdrift erosion is not an issue) • Beach nourishment (with future top-ups/re-cycling, and possibly buried gabion or rock revetment) • Rock revetment (gabions or timber if a 10-15 year life is acceptable) • Plus minor works to enhance appearance/habitat (i.e. fencing, planting, thatching, re-cycling) NB if erosion is long term backshore assets should not be enhanced or replaced, thereby allowing for ultimate abandonment	£50,000 - £200,000	• Rock groynes to deflect flow (possibly with beach nourishment and future top-ups) • Dredging and re-cycling to after flow regime • Gabion or rock revetment • Plus minor works to delay losses between structures (i.e. fencing, planting, thatching, beach re-cycling, gabion revetments)	£20,000 - £100,000
High economic value and long residual life (>25 years) (High density housing, railways, main roads, industrial facilities, power stations, etc)	Large rock revetments (possibly with groynes and/or beach nourishment with future top-ups/ re-cycling), plus minor works to enhance appearance/habitat (i.e. fencing, planting, thatching, recycling)	£100,000 - £300,000	• Large gabion or rock revetment with groynes to deflect flows (possibly with beach nourishment and future top ups)	£50,000 - £200,000

Table 5.2 Relative costs, life expectancy and potential environmental impacts associated with shoreline management options

(* = low, ***** = high)

Option	Impacts [1]				Costs		
	Habitat	Landform	Landscape	Processes	Capital	Maintenance[2]	Life Expectancy[3]
Adaptive management	**	**	**	*	Dependant on assets	*	*****
Grass planting	*	*	*	*	*	***	*
Thatching	*	*	*	*	*	***	*
Fencing	*	*	**	*	*	***	*
Beach recycling	**	*	*	*	**	***	*
Sandbag structures	**	**	**	**	**	*	**
Beach drainage	*	*	*	**	***	**	*
Beach nourishment	**	*	*	*	***	***	**
Gabion revetments [4]	***	***	***	***	***	**	***
Artificial headlands	**	**	***	***	***	*	***
Artificial reefs	**	**	***	***	***	*	***
Nearshore breakwaters	***	**	****	***	***	*	***
Groynes	***	***	***	***	***	*	***
Rock revetments [4]	****	****	*****	****	****	*	*****
Timber revetments [4]	***	***	****	***	****	*	***
Impermeable revetments/ seawalls	****	*****	*****	****	*****	*	****

(1)   Impacts over full life-cycle of option

(2)   Maintenance cost relative to capital cost (to retain design benefits)

(3)   Life expectancy of benefits without maintenance

(4)   If buried into the dune face the impacts associated with these approaches are lowered and the life expectancy increased; capital costs may be higher but maintenance costs lower.

6. References and Bibliography

6.1 Scottish regional information

THE BEACHES OF SCOTLAND SERIES

(prepared by Dept. of Geography, University of Aberdeen, for the Countryside Commission for Scotland).

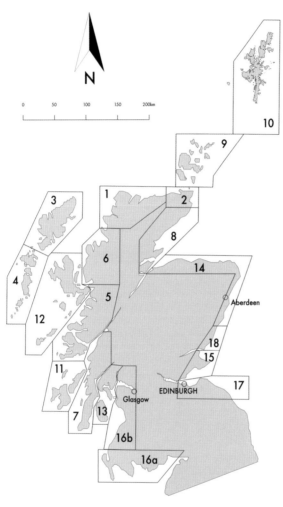

Figure 6.1   Location of regions covered by "The Beaches of Scotland Series (1969-1981)"

Map No.	Report Title. The Beaches of...	Authors	Date
1	Sutherland	Ritchie, W & Mather, AS	1969
2	Caithness	Ritchie, W & Mather, AS	1970
3	Lewis & Harris	Ritchie, W & Mather, AS	1970
4	Barra & the Uists	Ritchie, W	1971
5	West Inverness-shire & North Argyll	Mather, AS & Crofts, R	1971
6	Wester Ross	Crofts, R & Mather, AS	1971
7	Mainland Argyll	Crofts, R & Ritchie, W	1973
8	East Sutherland & Easter Ross	Smith, JS and Mather, AS	1973
9	Orkney	Mather, AS, Smith, JS & Ritchie, W	1973
10	Shetland	Mather, AS & Smith, JS	1974
11	Islay, Jura & Colonsay	Ritchie, W & Crofts, R	1973
12	Northern Inner Hebrides	Mather, AS, Smith, JS & Ritchie, W	1974
13	Cowal Bute & Arran	Ritchie, W	1974
14	North East Scotland	Ritchie, W, Smith, JS & Rose, N	1978
15	Fife	Ritchie, W	1979
16a	South West Scotland Volume II (Solway Firth)	Mather, AS	1979
16b	South West Scotland Volume I (Firth of Clyde)	Mather, AS	1979
17	Southeast Scotland	Rose, N	1980
18	Tayside	Wright, R	1981

THE COASTAL CELLS OF SCOTLAND SERIES

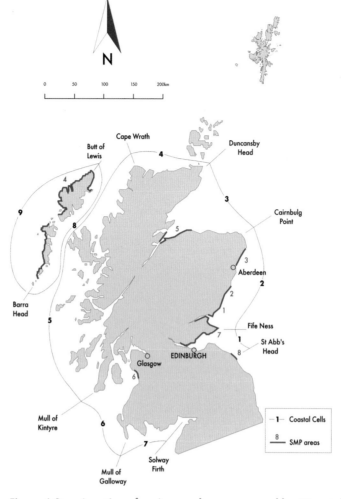

Figure 6.2   Location of regions and areas covered by "Coastal Cells of Scotland" series and Shoreline Management Plans and analogous studies

1   HR Wallingford, 2000. *Coastal Cells in Scotland. Cell 1 – St Abb's Head to Fife Ness.* Report to Scottish Natural Heritage, Scottish Office (Agriculture, Environment and Fisheries Dept.) and Historic Scotland. SNH RSM Report No. 143. Battleby.

2   HR Wallingford, 2000. *Coastal Cells in Scotland. Cell 2 - Fife Ness to Cairnbulg Point.* Report to Scottish Natural Heritage, Scottish Office (Agriculture, Environment and Fisheries Dept.) and Historic Scotland. SNH RSM Report No. 144. Battleby.

3   HR Wallingford, 2000. *Coastal Cells in Scotland. Cell 3 - Cairnbulg Point to Duncansby Head.* Report to Scottish Natural Heritage, Scottish Office (Agriculture, Environment and Fisheries Dept.) and Historic Scotland. SNH RSM Report No. 145. Battleby.

4   HR Wallingford, 2000. *Coastal Cells in Scotland. Cell 4 – Duncansby Head to Cape Wrath.* Report to Scottish Natural Heritage, Scottish Office (Agriculture, Environment and Fisheries Dept.) and Historic Scotland. SNH RSM Report No. 146. Battleby.

5   HR Wallingford, 2000. *Coastal Cells in Scotland. Cell 5 – Cape Wrath to the Mull of Kintyre.* Report to Scottish Natural Heritage, Scottish Office (Agriculture, Environment and Fisheries Dept.) and Historic Scotland. SNH RSM Report No. 147. Battleby.

6   HR Wallingford, 2000. *Coastal Cells in Scotland. Cell 6 – Mull of Kintyre to the Mull of Galloway.* Report to Scottish Natural Heritage, Scottish Office (Agriculture, Environment and Fisheries Dept.) and Historic Scotland. SNH RSM Report No. 148. Battleby.

7   HR Wallingford, 2000. *Coastal Cells in Scotland. Cell 7 – Mull of Galloway to the Inner Solway Firth.* Report to Scottish Natural Heritage, Scottish Office (Agriculture, Environment and Fisheries Dept.) and Historic Scotland. SNH RSM Report No. 149. Battleby.

8/9 HR Wallingford, 2000. *Coastal Cells in Scotland. Cell 8 & 9 – The Western Isles.* Report to Scottish Natural Heritage, Scottish Office (Agriculture, Environment and Fisheries Dept.) and Historic Scotland. SNH RSM Report No. 150. Battleby.

10   HR Wallingford, 2000. *Coastal Cells in Scotland. Cell 10 - Orkney.* Report to Scottish Natural Heritage, Scottish Office (Agriculture, Environment and Fisheries Dept.) and Historic Scotland. SNH RSM Report No. 151. Battleby.

11   HR Wallingford, 2000. *Coastal Cells in Scotland. Cell 11 -Shetland.* Report to Scottish Natural Heritage, Scottish Office (Agriculture, Environment and Fisheries Dept.) and Historic Scotland. SNH RSM Report No. 152. Battleby.

SHORELINE MANAGEMENT PLANS AND SHORELINE ASSESSMENTS

1   Caledonian Geotech, 1987. *Tayside Regional Council, Coastal Erosion Study. Phase 2. Final Report.* Unpublished report to Tayside Regional Council. Dundee.

2   Halcrow Crouch, 1998. *Montrose Bay Shoreline Management Study.* Unpublished report to Angus Council and Glaxo Wellcome (2 volumes). November 1997 and January 1998.

3   Halcrow Crouch, 1999. *Aberdeen Bay Coastal Protection Study. Final Report.* Unpublished report to Aberdeen City Council, Scottish Natural Heritage and Grampian Enterprise. September 1999. Aberdeen City Council, Aberdeen.

4   HR Wallingford, 1995. *Survey of Coastal Erosion in the Western Isles.* Unpublished report to Scottish Natural Heritage, the Western Isles Islands Council and the Minch Project. HR Wallingford Report EX 3155. 1995.

5   HR Wallingford, 1996. *Shoreline Management Plan. Inverness Firth and part of Moray Firth (Burghead to Sutors).* Unpublished report to Highland Regional Council. HR Wallingford Report EX 3230. September 1996.

6   HR Wallingford, 1996. *Saltcoats to Troon. Coastal Processes and Development.* Unpublished report to Scottish Natural Heritage and Strathclyde Regional Council. HR Wallingford Report EX 3327. October 1996.

7   Posford Duvivier, 1998. *Shoreline Management Plan of Fife.* Unpublished report to Fife Council (3 volumes). June 1998. Fife Council, Glenrothes.

8   Posford Duvivier, 1998. *St Abb's Head to The Tyne Shoreline Management Plan.* Unpublished report to Wansbeck Council.

6.2 Further guidance for dune management

Adriani, M J & Terwindt, J H J (1974). *Sand stabilization and dune building.* Rijkswaterstaat Commun., no. 19, The Hague.

ASH (1994). *Coastal erosion and tourism in Scotland: A review of protection measures to combat coastal erosion related to tourist activities and facilities.* SNH Review No 12. Scottish Natural Heritage, Perth.

Boorman, L A (1977). Sand dunes. In Barnes, R S K (ed). *The Coastline.* John Wiley and Sons.

British Trust for Conservation Volunteers (1986). *Fencing. Practical Conservation Handbook.* London.

British Trust for Conservation Volunteers (1979) *Coastlands. A practical conservation handbook.* London.

British Trust for Conservation Volunteers (1996). *Dunes. A practical handbook.* London.

Carter, R W G (1980). Vegetation stabilization and slope failure of eroding sand dunes. *Biol. Conserv.*, 18, 117-122.

CERC (1981). *Low Cost Shore Protection (Final Report on the Shoreline Erosion Control Demonstration Program).* Office, Chief of Engineers, U. S. Army Corps of Engineers, Washington, D. C.

D'Angremond, K, van den Berg, E J F & de Jager, J H (1992). Use and behaviour of gabions in coastal protection. Coastal Engineering, *ASCE*, 1748-1757.

Delft Hydraulics (1987). *Manual on artificial beach nourishment.* Delft Hydraulics Report 130. Rijkswaterstaat.

Doody, J P (1989). Management for nature conservation. *Proceedings of the Royal Society of Edinburgh*, 96B, 247-265pp.

East Lothian County Council (1970). *Dune conservation. A twenty year record of work in East Lothian.* East Lothian County Council, Council Planning Dept. Haddington.

ECOPRO (1996). *Environmentally friendly coastal protection: Code of practice.* Stationery Office, Dublin.

Janssen, M P (1995). Coastal Management: Restoration of Natural Processes in Foredunes. In: Healy M G and Doody J P (eds), *Directions in European Coastal Management*, Samara Publishing Ltd, pp. 195-197.

McConnell, K (1998). *Revetment systems against wave attack – A design manual.* Thomas Telford, London.

Mather, A S & Ritchie, W (1977). *The beaches of the Highlands and Islands of Scotland.* Countryside Commission for Scotland. Perth.

Motyka, J M & Brampton, A H (1994). *Effectiveness of beach control operations.* HR Wallingford Report SR 402.

Motyka, J M & Welsby, J (1983). *A review of novel shore protection methods. Volume 1 – use of scrap types.* Hydraulics Research Limited Report No IT 249.

Motyka, J M & Welsby, J (1984). *A review of novel shore protection methods. Volume 2 – sand and mortar filled fabric bags.* Hydraulics Research Limited Report No IT 253.

Motyka, J M & Welsby, J (1986). *A review of novel shore protection methods. Inspection of sea defences in Holland and Belgium*, 17 to 21 September 1984. Hydraulics Research Limited Report No SR 6.

Phillips, C J (1975). *Review of selected literature on sand stabilisation.* Dept. of Engineering, University of Aberdeen (unpub.).

Phillips, C J & Willetts, B B (1978). A review of selected literature on sand stabilization. *Coast. Eng.*, 2, 133-148.

Posford Duvivier Environment (1996). *The role of dune management in coastal defence: an environmental, technical and economic evaluation.* Unpub. report to CCW. 2 volumes. 161pp. (+ Appendices)

Ranwell, D S (ed) (1974). *Sand Dune Machair.* Institute of Terrestrial Ecology, Natural Environment Research Council. Report of a seminar at the Coastal Ecology Research Station, Norwich.

Ranwell, D S & Boar, R (1986). *Coast dune management guide.* Institute of Terrestrial Ecology. NERC.

Ritchie, W (1972). The evolution of coastal sand dunes. *Scottish Geographical Magazine*, 88, 91-105.

Ritchie, W (1975). Environmental Problems Associated with a Pipeline Landfall in Coastal Dunes at Cruden Bay, Aberdeenshire, Scotland. *Coastal Engineering*, 3, 2568-79.

Ritchie, W (1978). The economic viability of some coastal dunes. *Shore and Beach*, 46, 21-24.

Ritchie, W (1981). Environmental aspects of oil and gas pipeline landfalls in north east Scotland. *Proc. 17th int. Coastal Engineering Conf., Sydney, Australia, 1980*, 2938-2954. New York: American Society of Engineers.

Ritchie, W & Mather, AS (1984). *The beaches of Scotland.* Countryside Commission for Scotland, Battleby, Perth. 130pp.

Robertson-Rintoul, M & Ritchie, W (1990). The Geomorphology of coastal sand dunes in Scotland. A review. *Catena Supplement* 18, 41-49.

Savage, R P & Woodhouse, W W (1968). Creation and stabilisation of coastal barrier dunes. *Proc. 11th int. Coastal Engineering Conf., London, 1968*, 671-700. New York: American Society of Civil Engineers.

Salmon, J, Henninghsen, D & McAlpin, T (1982). *Dune restoration and revegetation manual.* Gainseville, Florida, USA.

Welsby, J & Motyka, J M (1985). *A review of novel shore protection methods. Volume 3 – gabions.* Hydraulics Research Limited Report No SR 5.

Welsby, J & Motyka, J M (1986). *A review of novel shore protection methods. Volume 4 – revetments.* Hydraulics Research Limited Report No SR 12.

Welsby, J & Motyka, J M (1986). *A review of novel shore protection methods. Volume 5 - offshore breakwaters and sills.* Hydraulics Research Limited Report No SR 34.

Wilcock, F A & Carter, R W G (1977). An environmental approach to the restoration of badly eroded sand dunes. *Biol. Conserv.*, 11, 279-291.

6.3 Coastal processes and shoreline management

Bruun, P (1983). Beach scraping: is it damaging to beach stability? *Coastal Engineering* 7, 167-173, Elsevier.

Carter, R W G (1988). *Coastal Environments.* Academic Press. London.

Carter, R W G. (1980). Human activities and geomorphic processes: the example of recreation pressure on the Northern Ireland coast. *Z. Geomorph.*, n.s. 34 (Suppl.), 155-164.

CERC (1984). *Shore Protection Manual.* U. S. Army Corps of Engineers, Coastal Engineering Research Center. Washington, D. C.

CIRIA (1996). *Beach Management Manual.* CIRIA Report 153. Construction Industry Research and Information Association.

CIRIA/CUR (1991). *Manual on the use of rock in coastal and shoreline engineering.* CIRIA Special Publication 83/ CUR Report 154. Construction Industry Research and Information Association.

Hansom, J D (1988). *Coasts.* Cambridge University Press. 96pp.

Hansom, J D, Crick, M & John, S (1999). *The potential application of Shoreline Management Planning to Scotland.* Scottish Natural Heritage Review No. 121. Scottish Natural Heritage, Perth.

HR Wallingford (1991). *A Guide to The Selection of Appropriate Coast Protection Words for Geological Sites of Special Scientific Interest.* Report No. EX 2112, Wallingford. 83pp.

Kana, W T & Svetlichny M (1982). Artificial manipulation of beach profiles. *Proc. Coastal Engineering Conference*, Cape Town.

MAFF (1993a). *Coastal defence and the environment: A guide to good practice.* Flood and Coastal Defence Division, MAFF. London. Report 1191.

MAFF (1993b). *Flood and coastal defence: Project appraisal guidance notes.* Flood and Coastal Defence Division, MAFF. London. Report PB 1214.

MAFF (1993c). *Shoreline Management Plans. Interim guidance on contents and procedures for developing SMPs.* Flood and Coastal Defence Division, MAFF. London.

MAFF (1995). *Shoreline Management Plans. A guide for coastal defence authorities.* Flood and Coastal Defence Division, MAFF. London. PB 2197.

MAFF (1997). *Interim guidance for the strategic planning and appraisal of flood and coastal defence schemes.* Flood and Coastal Defence Division, MAFF. London.

MAFF (1998). *Shoreline Management Plans. Advisory Notes Nos 1-12.* Unpub. Interim Guidance Prepared by the SMP Advisory Group. Flood and Coastal Defence Division, MAFF. London.

Motyka, J M & Brampton, A H (1993). *Coastal management. Mapping of littoral cells.* Unpub. rep to MAFF. Hydraulics Research Wallingford. Report SR 328. 102pp.

Nash, E (1962). *Beach and sand dune erosion control at Cape Hatteras National Seashore: a five year review (1956-1961).* Manteo, NC: National Park Service.

Pethick, J (1984). *An Introduction to Coastal Geomorphology.* Edward Arnold, London. 250pp.

Pilarczyk, K W (1990). Design of seawalls and dikes, including overview of revetments. In: *Coastal Protection, Proceedings of the short course on coastal protection.* Delft University of Technology. A A Balkema, Rotterdam, Brookfield.

Pilarczyk, K W (1995). Geotextiles systems for coastal protection. *Int. Conf. Coastal and Port Engineering in Developing Countries, Brazil.*

Scottish Office (1997). *National Planning Policy Guideline 13. Coastal planning.* Scottish Office Development Department.

Steers, J A (1969). *The Sea Coast.* Collins New Naturalist.

Steers, J A (1973). *The Coastline of Scotland.* Cambridge University Press.

Swash, A R H, Leafe, R N & Radley, G P (1995). Shoreline Management Plans and Environmental Considerations. In: Healy, MG and Doody, JP (eds), *Directions in European Coastal Management*, Samara Publishing Ltd, Cardigan. 161-167.

Thomas, R S & Hall, B (1992). *Seawall design.* Prepared for CIRIA. Butterworths, London.

Tye, R S (1983). Impact of Hurricane David and Mechanical Dune Restoration on Folly Beach, South Carolina. *Shore & Beach*, April 1983.

Viles, H & Spencer, T (1995). *Coastal Problems: Geomorphology, Ecology and Society at the Coast.* Edward Arnold, London, 350pp.

7. Glossary of terms and abbreviations

7.1 Glossary

A Class tide gauge	One of a UK network of tide gauges maintained to the highest and most consistent standards.
Accretion	The accumulation of (beach) sediment, deposited by natural processes.
Apron	Layers of stone, concrete or other material to protect the toe of a structure such as a **seawall**.
Armour unit	Large quarried stone, or concrete block, used as protection against wave action.
Backshore	Coastal area between the **beach head** and high water, potentially affected by large waves during high tides.
Barrier beach	A sand or shingle bar above high tide, parallel to the coastline and separated from it by a lagoon.
Bathymetry	Seabed topography.
Beach	A deposit of non-cohesive mobile material (e.g. sand, gravel) situated on the interface between dry land and the sea (or other expanses of water).
Beach face	From the beach crest out to the limit of sediment movement.
Beach head	Ridge, cliff, dune or sea defence forming the landward limit of the potentially active beach
Beach profile	Beach cross-section perpendicular to the shore, which may extend from the backshore, across the foreshore and into the **nearshore zone**.
Beach recharge	Mechanical addition of imported sediment to a beach, also known as beach replenishment/ nourishment.
Berm	Beach: near horizontal plateau above high water, formed by deposition of beach material by wave action or by mechanical plant as part of a beach recharge scheme. Structure: near horizontal area, often separating the upper part of a seawall or revetment from the lower part.
Binding	Use of chemical glues to create a skin across a sediment surface. Usually applied by spraying.
Blowout	Wind-eroded area within a dune system.
Boulder	A rounded rock on a beach, greater than 250mm in diameter.
Breaching	Failure of the **beach head** allowing flooding by tidal action.
Breaker zone	The zone within which waves approaching the coastline commence breaking, typically in water depths of between 5 and 10 metres.
Breastwork	Vertically faced or steeply inclined structure built parallel to the shoreline, at or near the crest of the beach, to resist erosion, usually timber.
Breakwater	Large coastal structure designed to protect an area from wave action, either for navigation or coastal defence. Can be connected to or detached from the shoreline.
Bypassing	Moving beach material from the **updrift** to the **downdrift** side of an obstruction to **longshore drift** i.e. harbour breakwater, estuary or river mouth.
Chart datum	The level to which both tidal levels and water depths are reduced – on most UK charts this level is approximately the predicted lowest astronomical tide level (LAT).
Coastal cell	See **Sediment cell**
Coastal defence	General term used to encompass both coast protection against erosion and sea defence against flooding.
Coast protection	Works or management operations intended to control coastal erosion
Coastal processes	Collective term covering the action of natural forces on the shoreline, and nearshore seabed.
Coastal squeeze	The effect when hard defences (including beaches fixed in position by control structures) interrupt the natural response of the shoreline to sea level rise, restricting landward retreat and resulting in loss of the intertidal habitat.
Cobble	A rounded rock on a beach, with diameter ranging from about 75 to 250mm – see also **boulder, gravel, shingle**.
Cohesive sediment	Sediment containing significant proportion of clays, the electromagnetic properties of which cause the sediment to bind together.
Community	Plants and/or animals living together under characteristic, recognisable conditions.
Core	An inner, often much less permeable portion of a breakwater, or barrier beach.
Crest	Highest point on a beach face, breakwater or seawall.
Cross-shore	Perpendicular to the shoreline.
Deflation	Erosion of dunes by wind action.
Design wave condition	Usually an extreme wave condition with a specified **return period** used in the design of coastal works.
Detached breakwater	A **breakwater** without any constructed connection to the shore.
Diffraction	Process affecting wave propagation, by which wave energy is radiated normal to the direction of wave propagation into the lee of an island or breakwater.
Dominant winds	Winds with greatest effect on shoreline processes.
Downdrift	Direction to which material is being transported in the **littoral zone**.
Dunes	Accumulations of windblown sand on the backshore, usually in the form of small hills or ridges, stabilised by vegetation or control structures.

Dune face	The seaward face of a dune system where coastal processes may cause erosion or accretion.
Ebb	Period when tide level is falling; often taken to mean the ebb current that occurs during this period.
Embankment	A bank protecting land from flooding.
Estuary	A semi-enclosed coastal body of water within which seawater is measurably diluted with fresh water derived from land drainage.
Extreme	The value expected to be exceeded once, on average, in a given (long) period of time.
Fetch	Distance over which a wind acts to produce waves – also termed fetch length.
Fetch-limited	Situation in which wave energy (or wave height) is limited by the size of the wave generation area (fetch).
Fixed dune	Dune with a surface stabilised by vegetation.
Foredune	Developing dune which lies nearest the sea in a prograding system, also embryo-dune.
Foreshore	Shore between high and low water – see also **intertidal**.
Freeboard	The height of the crest of a structure above the still water level.
Gabion	Wire mesh baskets filled with rock.
Geotextile	Synthetic or natural fabrics used in engineering to separate layers of granular material.
Gravel	Beach material usually well rounded and between about 2mm and 75mm in diameter – see also **shingle**.
Grey dune	Well-vegetated fixed dune with mosses, lichens, grasses and herbs.
Groyne	Narrow, shore-normal (approximately) structure built to reduce longshore currents, and/or to trap and retain beach material. Most groynes are of timber or rock, and extend from the **beach head** across the foreshore.
Groyne bay	The beach compartment between two groynes.
Habitat	The recognisable area or type of environment in which an organism normally lives.
Hard defences	General term applied to impermeable coastal defence structures of concrete, timber, steel, masonry etc, which reflect a high proportion of incident wave energy. cf. Soft defences
Headland	Hard feature (natural or artificial) forming local limit of longshore extent of a beach.
Intertidal	The zone between high and low tide lines – see also **foreshore**.
Joint probability	The probability of two (or more) events occurring together.
Leach	The process by which percolating water removes nutrients from the soil
Littoral drift	Movement of beach material in the **littoral zone** under the influence of waves and currents.
Littoral zone	Zone from the **beach head** seawards to the limit of wave induced sediment movement.
Longshore drift	Movement of (beach) sediments approximately parallel to the coastline.
Machair	Sandy coastal plain, typically calcareous (as found in northwest Scotland).
Macro-tidal	Tidal range greater than 4m.
Meso-tidal	Tidal range between 2m and 4m.
Micro-tidal	Tidal range less than 2m.
Mud flat	An area of fine silt usually exposed at low tide but covered at high tide, occurring in sheltered estuaries or behind shingle bars or sand spits.
Mulching	Mixing organic material into the sediment surface to reduce erosion, moisten the surface and fertilise the soil.
Natural succession	The process by which one community of organisms gives way to another in an orderly series from colonisers to climax.
Neap tide	Tide of least range in the tidal cycle.
Nearshore	Areas where waves are transformed by interaction with the sea bed.
Numerical modelling	Refers to the analysis or prediction of coastal processes using computational models.
Offshore	The zone beyond the **nearshore** zone where sediment motion induced by waves alone effectively ceases and where the influence of the sea bed on wave action has become small in comparison with the effect of wind.
Overwash	The effect of waves overtopping a beach, often carrying sediment landwards
Physical modelling	Refers to the investigation of coastal processes using a scaled model.
Pocket beach	A beach located between two **headlands**.
Prevailing winds	Winds of greatest frequency, often but not always the **dominant winds**.
Prograding	Developing along the shore or into open water.
Reef	A ridge of rock, or other material, lying seawards of the low water line.
Refraction	Process by which the direction of a wave moving in shallow water at an angle to the bathymetric contours is changed so that the wave crests tend to become more aligned with those contours.
Regrading	The mechanical movement of beach sediment from the lower foreshore to the upper foreshore – see also **reprofiling**.
Reprofiling	The mechanical movement of beach sediment from downdrift to updrift – see also **regrading**.
Return period	Average period of time between occurrences of a given probability event.
Revetment	A sloping surface of stone, concrete or other material, used to protect the shoreline against the sea.
Rhizome	Fleshy root-ball of plant from which roots and side shoots develop.
Run-up, Run-down	The upper and lower levels reached by a wave on a beach or coastal structure, relative to still-water level.

Salient	Coastal formation of beach material developed by wave refraction and diffraction and longshore drift comprising a bulge in the coastline towards an offshore island or breakwater, but not connected to it as in the case of a **tombolo**.
Salt marsh	Intertidal area having characteristic vegetation adapted to saline soils and to periodic submergence in sea water.
Sand	Sediment particles, mainly of quartz, with a diameter of between 0.062mm and 2mm, generally classified as fine, medium, coarse or very coarse
Sea defence	Works or management operations intended to prevent coastal flooding
Seawall	Solid near vertical coastal defence structure built parallel to the coastline, usually of concrete or masonry.
Sediment	Particulate matter derived from rock, minerals or shell debris.
Sediment cell	In the context of a strategic approach to coastal management, a length of coastline confined by natural or artificial barriers around which no sand or shingle can be transported – also know as **coastal cell**.
Sediment sink	Point or area at which beach material is irretrievably lost from a **sediment cell**, such as an **estuary**, or a deep channel in the seabed.
Sediment source	Point or area on a coast from which beach material arises, such as an eroding cliff, or river mouth.
Shingle	Coarse grained beach sediment dominated by gravel but including some sand.
Shoreline	One characteristic of the coast, often poorly defined, but essentially the interface between land and sea.
Shoreline management	The development of strategic, long-term and sustainable coastal defence policy within a **sediment cell**.
Significant wave height	Measured as the average height of the highest third of the waves in a sea, and is approximately the visually observed wave height (H_s or H).
Sill	Continuous shore parallel structure, submerged at high tide.
Silt	Sediment particles with a grain size between 0.004mm and 0.062mm i.e. coarser than clay particles but finer than sand.
Slack	Area within dune system where the surface is at or near the ground water level.
Soft defences	Usually refers to managed beaches, saltmarshes or mudflats that provide protection to the shoreline, but may also include rock structures which dissipate waves rather than opposing them. cf. Hard defences
Spring tide	Tide of greatest range in a monthly cycle.
Spit	A long, narrow accumulation of sand or shingle, lying generally in line with the coast, with one end attached to the land and the other projecting into the sea or across the mouth of an **estuary**.
Strand line	Line of debris formed at the limit of wave run up along the upper foreshore.
Surge	Changes in water level as a result of meteorological forcing (wind, high or low barometric pressure) causing a difference between the recorded water level and that predicted using harmonic analysis; may be positive or negative.
Suspended load	A mode of sediment transport in which the particles are supported, and carried along by water.
Swash zone	The zone of wave action on the beach, which moves as water levels vary, extending from the limit of **run-down** to the limit of **run-up**.
Swell (waves)	Remotely wind-generated waves. Swell characteristically exhibits a more regular and longer period and has longer crests than locally generated waves – see also **wind sea**.
Surf zone	The zone of wave action extending from the water line (which varies with tide, surge, set-up, etc.) out to the most seaward point of the zone (breaker zone) at which waves approaching the coastline commence breaking, typically in water depths of between 5 and 10 metres.
Tidal current	The movement of water associated with the rise and fall of the tides.
Tidal range	Vertical difference in high and low water level once decoupled from the water level residuals.
Tide	The periodic rise and fall in the level of the water in oceans and seas; the result of gravitational attraction of the sun and moon.
Tombolo	Coastal formation of beach material developed by **refraction**, **diffraction** and **longshore drift** to form a 'neck' connecting a coast to an offshore island or breakwater - see also **salient**.
Thatching	Covering of brushwood laid down to protect dune grasses and help trap sand.
Updrift	Direction from which material is being transported in the **littoral zone**.
Water table	Level below which the soil is waterlogged.
Wave climate	The seasonal and annual distribution of wave height, period and direction.
Wave direction	Mean direction of wave energy propagation relative to true North.
Wave height	Vertical distance from wave trough to crest.
Wave period	Time taken for the passage of successive waves past a point.
Wave spectrum	Distribution of wave energy as a function of wave frequency and direction.
Wave transformation	Change in wave energy due to the action of physical processes.
Wind rose	Diagram showing the long term distribution of wind speed and direction.
Wind sea	Wave conditions directly attributed to recent winds – see also **swell**.
Wind set-up	Elevation of the water level over an area directly caused by wind stress on the water surface.
Yellow dune	Incompletely vegetated dune with bare sand frequently exposed between plant stems.

7.2 Abbreviations

Organisations

BTCV	British Trust for Conservation Volunteers
CCS	Countryside Commission for Scotland
CPAu	Coast Protection Authority
MAFF	Ministry of Agriculture, Fisheries and Food
SEDD	Scottish Executive Development Department
SERAD	Scottish Executive Rural Affairs Department
SNH	Scottish Natural Heritage

Parliamentary Acts

CPA	Coast Protection Act, 1949
FEPA	Food and Environment Protection Act, 1985
TCPSA	Town and Country Planning (Scotland) Act, 1997
WCA	Wildlife and Countryside Act, 1981

Water levels

SWL	Still Water Level
HAT	Highest Astronomical Tide
MHWS	Mean High Water of Spring tide
HWMOST	High Water Mark of Ordinary Spring Tides
HWMONT	High Water Mark of Ordinary Neap Tides
MSL	Mean Sea Level
LWMONT	Low Water Mark of Ordinary Neap Tides
LWMOST	Low Water of Ordinary Spring Tides
MLWS	Mean Low Water of Spring tide
LAT	Lowest Astronomical Tide

Environmental designations

AGLV	Areas of Great Landscape Value
ESA	Environmentally Sensitive Area
LNR	Local Nature Reserve
MCA	Marine Consultation Area
MNR	Marine Nature Reserve
NHA	Natural Heritage Areas
NNR	National Nature Reserve
NSA	National Scenic Areas
Ramsar Sites	Wetland habitats site designated under the Ramsar Convention
SAC	Special Area of Conservation
SPA	Special Protection Area
SSSI	Site of Special Scientific Interest

Others

EA	Environmental Assessment
ES	Environmental Statement
GIS	Geographic Information System
GPS	Global Positioning System
OLD	Operations Likely to Damage
PA	Planning Authority
P Dev	Permitted Development

Appendix 1   Erosion management options

These summaries are intended as stand alone documents. They contain sufficient information to allow proposed schemes to be assessed and to guide non-specialists in the implementation of minor management projects. The summaries are not intended to replace the services of a competent coastal consultant for the design and implementation of larger schemes.

In order to provide a comprehensive guide to the options available for the management of coastal erosion all principle coast protection and erosion management techniques are covered. It must be recognised, however, that virtually all of these can be damaging to the natural environment, to a greater or lesser degree, in inappropriate situations. The inclusion of any particular approach herein does not, therefore, indicate that it is, necessarily, environmentally sensitive, nor that SNH considers it universally appropriate as a means of managing erosion. Rather, the summaries highlight and encourage the pursuit of good practice, from an environmental perspective, which ever approach is deemed necessary by the circumstances concerned.

Each summary contains a decision support table to highlight the main considerations of appropriate locations, guide costs (2000 prices), effectiveness, benefits and problems. This is followed by a general description, discussion of function, guide to methods, and a discussion of possible impacts, environmental opportunities and best practices.

Summary 1 sets out a discussion of the benefits of taking a minimal intervention approach. This should be reviewed with respect to any eroding dune site before other management approaches are considered.

Summaries 2 through 6 describe approaches that can be undertaken by non-specialists: costs are relatively low and the consequences of poor design or implementation are short term. If proposed schemes are of a large scale, the services of specialists should still be commissioned to ensure cost effective implementation based on a thorough understanding of the site conditions. These approaches can be used in combination to good effect, and can also be used in conjunction with the more costly options as a way of enhancing the recovery and growth of the dune face.

Summaries 7 through 16 set out approaches that require the services of specialist coastal consultants. The methods are costly and the consequences of improper design may be damaging to both the local shoreline and the wider coastal zone. None of these approaches should be implemented without a thorough understanding of the site, the likely future evolution of the shoreline and the long term costs and benefits.

Finally, summary 17 presents a brief description of a number of alternative approaches that have been tried both in the UK and abroad. In general, these options are considered to be of little value in the management of dune erosion in Scotland.

Summary 1: ADAPTIVE MANAGEMENT

APPROPRIATE LOCATIONS	Locations with low value, life expired or moveable backshore assets
COSTS	Depends on backshore assets
EFFECTIVENESS	Short term loss of assets, but highly sustainable over medium to long term
BENEFITS	Allows natural processes to continue with possible strategic benefits spread over adjacent areas. No ongoing management costs.
PROBLEMS	Backshore assets are lost or moved, often causing conflict due to differing perceptions of values

General description

Many cases of dune erosion may be best managed by not interfering with the natural processes, but instead accepting that erosion will occur and adapting backshore management accordingly. This approach will involve relocation and monitoring costs, but these may be much lower than the cost of protection.

Adaptive management should be considered at all sites before considering any of the other options set out in this guide.

Defend or adapt?

Function

Dune erosion is often cyclical with periods of loss balanced by periods of gain. Erosion may also not be constant alongshore, with areas of loss balanced by adjacent areas of gain. Works undertaken to arrest the rate of erosion at a specific site may be detrimental to subsequent natural recovery at that site, and may increase erosion along adjacent frontages. The nett result may well be accelerated long term shoreline recession. Alternatively defensive works, such as groynes or revetments, may become redundant if natural recovery causes the defences to be completely buried by sand. In either case the efforts to influence dune erosion would be either wasted or damaging.

Adapting to erosion, or the potential for erosion, by moving, replacing or demolishing structures or other assets that are at risk will avoid the need for interference with coastal processes. Better still is the initial control of any form of development along the shoreline dunes, though in many instances it will be too late to adopt this preventative approach.

Common assets at risk around Scottish dune systems are golf course tees and greens, amenity areas and footpaths, caravan sites and grazing land. Although these features may be viewed as essential to the character of the coast, the costs involved in re-siting or replacement could well be much lower, and more sustainable into the future, than the costs of constructing defences to protect them.

Methods

The decision to abandon or move backshore assets should be based on the actual or perceived value of the assets at risk, the costs of effective erosion management alternatives (including future maintenance costs) and the environmental acceptability of those defences. It must also be based on a clear understanding of the physical and biological processes affecting the beach/dune system and predictions of the likely future evolution of the shoreline. This understanding will require investment in studies of past shoreline evolution and existing conditions, combined with a monitoring programme to allow ongoing reassessment of the evolution predictions.

If management of marine erosion is being considered it is assumed that assets of value are being threatened. These assets may be natural, such as a rare habitat or a particularly interesting geomorphological feature. In general erosion of such features would be considered part of their natural evolution and therefore preferable to management interference. More often the assets will have socio-economic importance, ranging from amenity access to a beach up to an industrial complex or power station. The shoreline manager must start by considering the value of the assets that may be at risk, then try to establish an understanding of the likely future evolution of the beach/dune system. Finally the manager must determine whether it is better to lose/move the assets or attempt to prevent or reduce the erosion.

The value of the backshore may be assessed in economic terms, based on the present replacement cost of buildings, infrastructure or land. The assessment should also consider the wider values such as potential loss of jobs, transport routes, rare habitats, recreation or cultural heritage (i.e. archaeological sites). Within Scotland there is no formal procedure for undertaking the benefit analysis, allowing each case to be treated on its own merits. If a formal approach is required for high value sites the methods used by the Ministry of Agriculture, Fisheries and Food in England provide a useful model (MAFF, 1993b).

In some cases, such as remote Highland beaches, the value assessment may be relatively straightforward and may lead to the rapid conclusion that any works would need to be very low cost and directed more at short term recreation and habitat management rather than attempts to prevent marine erosion. In other cases, including areas on the east and south west coasts that are heavily developed for industry or housing, the decision may also be straightforward, leading to substantial investment in major permanent defence works. More commonly the users of this guide will be concerned with the complicated issues arising from situations lying between these two extremes.

Having formed an initial view on the value of the backshore the manager must consider the likely evolution of the shoreline, and the potential for any backshore flooding as a result of erosion. This is a difficult task as there is often a lack of data, and what there is will often be skewed towards the very recent past. It must be remembered that dune development can be measured over timescales of decades or centuries, whereas substantial erosion can occur in a single storm. The services of a specialist consultant are likely to be required for important or complicated sites.

Ideally, investigations will combine site monitoring over several years with a desk study of available data. Historic maps, charts, surveys and aerial photographs give an indication of long term rates of shoreline change, while engineering records may indicate whether changes are related to human interference or are indicative of

Clear felling of forestry along an eroding coastline. Mature trees can pull up large areas of soil when toppling; felling them in advance of coastal erosion minimises this damage and may reduce the rate of retreat.

natural trends. Wind, wave and water level records will provide evidence to assess the likely frequency of events leading to erosion or accretion, and will allow any recent storm related damage to be set into a long term context. Backshore topographic surveying of any lowlying areas will establish the potential for flooding in the event of dune breaching.

Often these investigations will lead to the conclusion that shoreline change is cyclical over periods ranging from seasons to decades, but that there is also an underlying trend of recession. Rapid erosion over a period of, say, five years will cause great concern to those interested in the backshore, but this may be preceded or followed by decades of accretion or stability. A panic response to the erosion may well lead to the construction of inappropriate and unnecessarily costly defences. A more reasoned response may be to recognise that the rapid erosion is an unusual fluctuation within a long term, gradual trend of recession. Continued rapid erosion may well be unlikely, but any management decision would have to recognise that the backshore assets will ultimately be at risk.

Having established a reasonable understanding of the coastal processes, a plan should be formulated for both short and long term management. In the short term it may be appropriate to initiate delaying tactics such as vegetation transplanting, dune fencing or beach recycling (Summaries 2 to 5). These activities can reduce the impacts of short term storm events, but are unlikely to reverse a long term trend of shoreline recession. Plans for the longer term may need to recognise likely recession rates and the importance of moving assets out of the risk areas.

Costs associated with adaptive management are site specific and can not be generalised. Accepting the gradual loss of a site valued as an undeveloped public recreation area may incur no actual cost at all apart from monitoring and minor works to delay erosion or encourage recovery (Summaries 2 to 5). At the other end of the scale the demolition and replacement of threatened shoreline buildings or recreational facilities may cost many thousands of pounds.

The alternative long term management approaches are to design and implement substantial and costly schemes, allowing for the future management of on-going local and regional erosion. These approaches are considered in Summaries 6 to 17.

Impact
Adaptive management will result in the controlled loss of backshore assets and the continued evolution of dune habitat and land form. This approach can be highly emotive, with local interest groups protesting vigorously and demanding that more positive actions be taken. However, it must be accepted that both erosion and accretion are natural elements of dune evolution, and that maintenance of natural evolution is, wherever possible, preferable to costly and environmentally disruptive intervention.

Best practice and environmental opportunities
Adaptive management minimises interference with the natural processes and ecosystem of an evolving dune system. Although a strict do-nothing approach could be taken, it may often be appropriate to implement short term works to manage and repair storm related erosion within a longer term policy of controlled adaptation. These complimentary approaches are discussed within option Summaries 2 to 5.

Monitoring, consultation and education are at the heart of adaptive management. The shoreline should be continuously assessed using data collected from site, combined with any available historic or published data. The monitoring will allow the management policy to be reviewed from time to time. Methods for appropriate beach/dune erosion monitoring are set out in Appendix 2 of this Guide. Impacts of the policy on recreation, land use and habitats should also be monitored.

Consultation is required to assess the values associated with the backshore, and to develop a consensus view on how to deal with the assets. This process is firmly linked with education, requiring the manager to set out the background issues in a language that can be readily appreciated by those who are affected.

Those responsible for the management of eroding dunes should be aware of the potential danger to the public of a collapsing dune face. Dangers exist both from falling down the face and from being buried at the base. Warning signs set up along the crest and at public access points should be the minimum response to these dangers.

Adaptive management should be incorporated into a long term coastal zone management programme that includes land use planning and environmental management over an area that may well extend beyond the immediate dunes. The approach allows for the sustainable, long term management of the shore, with no commitment to costly or environmentally disruptive engineered schemes.

Summary 2:   DUNE GRASS PLANTING

APPROPRIATE LOCATIONS	Above normal limit of wave run-up at any location with available blown sand. Unlikely to succeed where erosion is severe.
COSTS	Low, but labour intensive with on-going management (£200 - £2000/100m length for each visit).
EFFECTIVENESS	Enhancement to natural dune recovery. Reservoir of sand held in planted foredunes will provide a buffer to resist storm erosion.
BENEFITS	Compliments natural system. Can be used to improve other management options. Potentially self sustaining.
PROBLEMS	Normally requires dune fencing or thatching to achieve success. May be completely lost to storm erosion.

General description

Vegetation encourages dune growth by trapping and stabilising blown sand. Transplanting marram grass (*Ammophila arenaria*) to the face of eroded dunes will enhance the natural development of yellow dunes above the limit of direct wave attack. Sand couchgrass (*Elymus farctus*) or lyme grass (*Leymus arenarius*) can be transplanted to encourage the growth of new foredunes along the toe of existing dunes, as these species are tolerant to occasional inundation by seawater. Planting grasses from seed can be undertaken but will not normally be successful in the very active foredune environment.

These natural dune grasses act to reduce wind speeds across the surface, thereby trapping and holding sand. They grow both vertically and horizontally as the sand accumulates. Marram grass is particularly effective as it positively thrives on growing dunes, and is perhaps the easiest to transplant.

Dune stabilisation using marram and lyme grass transplants.

Function

Transplanting vegetation will not prevent erosion, but it will accelerate natural recovery after storm damage creating a reservoir of sand within the foredunes that will make the dunes better able to withstand the next period of erosion. Additional works are often necessary to increase the potential for success. Thatching (Summary 3), fencing (Summary 4) and beach recycling (Summary 5) will assist in the accretion of sand, will provide minor protection from waves and will reduce damage due to trampling. Once grasses are well established they may well become self-sustaining, although any storm erosion damage will need to be rapidly made good.

Potential borrow areas for small schemes on lee side of yellow dunes (roots less developed, blow out risk less severe)

Marram and lyme grass transplanted at 0.2m-0.9m intervals above storm wave run-up limit. Lyme grass and sand couchgrass transplanted down to normal limit of wave run-up

Dune fencing to encourage accretion

Normal limit of wave run-up

Sand from recycling or accreted due to fencing (maximum slope about 1:2). Alternatively existing eroding face can be re-profiled to a shallower slope.

Posts driven to 1m below lowest expected beach level

Transplanting dune grasses to an eroded dune face

Transplanting can also be used to enhance the appearance and effectiveness of built erosion defences. Rock, timber or gabion structures can provide a fixed defence line but are incongruous along a natural dune coast: partial burial of these structures using recycled sand, followed by transplanting, will create a more natural dune appearance if conditions are favourable. However transplanting to inappropriate locations can be a waste of resources, as illustrated in the photograph below.

Methods

The subject of dune vegetation transplanting is covered in detail within various publications, including the British Trust for Conservation Volunteers "Sand Dunes Handbook". It is common practice in the management of wind erosion and recreational pressures and has been undertaken at many sites. Essentially, vigorous plants are pulled or dug up from a suitable borrow area, and are replanted on an eroded face, where they will be immediately effective in trapping blown sand. Where stock, such as sheep or cattle, can gain access to the replanted site these may cause considerable damage through grazing and trampling of the transplanted grasses. Growth and stabilisation will often only be realised once these have been excluded, for instance through fence construction. Additional works such as re-profiling of steep or unstable faces, fencing or thatching should be done in advance to avoid damaging the transplants. These complimentary approaches are discussed in Summaries 3 to 5. Without these works, transplanting is unlikely to be successful unless natural recovery is well underway. The basic principles of transplanting are illustrated above.

Marram grass is tolerant of salt spray but not immersion, and should be planted above the expected run-up limit of storm waves. Lyme grass can tolerate occasional inundation and can be transplanted down to the beach dune interface. In practice there is little point in trying to extend the vegetation cover too far as wave damage may quickly remove the lowest transplants before they have a chance to take root.

Common dune grasses.

a) marram grass

b) lyme grass

50

Transplanting should not be seen as a one-off operation. Regular maintenance is required to replace unhealthy plants, apply fertilisers, prevent trampling and extend cover to adjacent areas. Work can be undertaken at any time of year, but early spring is generally considered to be the optimum to avoid frosts, storm erosion, drought or trampling. Even assuming no storm erosion, it is likely that it will take two or three years before transplants begin to thrive and spread.

For small schemes transplants may be taken locally, ensuring that the borrow area is not denuded to the extent that blow outs may form. Larger schemes require a commercial supply or a managed nursery area within the dune system. Forward planning is required to ensure that sufficient seedlings and/or mature plants are available for transplanting. Sowing dune grass seeds is not a practical solution to marine erosion, but can be applied successfully to more stable backshore dunes, if considered necessary.

Costs for transplanting are dependent on labour, sources of transplants, extent of works, the need for ongoing management and the cost of ancillary works to help stabilise the dune face. Small schemes implemented by volunteer labour using local transplants may cost almost nothing, while extensive schemes using commercial nursery transplants and contracted labour may cost up to £20,000/km, plus ongoing management costs. Cost assessment should allow for the possibility that the transplant scheme may be substantially damaged by the first storm event following the works.

Marram planted to landward of a large rock revetment lacks vigour as it is starved of blown sand.

Impacts

Transplanting and management of appropriate dune grasses to the dune face will have no damaging impact on the natural environment of the receiving area, but can be harmful to the borrow area. Over harvesting of transplants from any area can give rise to increased local erosion. This may be most significant for sand couch grass, as the borrow area will necessarily be a foredune susceptible to wave over-washing and wind erosion.

Construction of fences or thatching will disrupt public use of the beach, so provision must be made for controlled access.

Five years on from planting, marram is thriving on this dune face.

Best practice and environmental opportunities

New vegetation cover to an eroding dune face will encourage recovery without damaging the ecological and geomorphological interests or the aesthetic appeal of the shoreline. The approach is potentially self-sustaining if the grasses become well established.

Transplanting and associated dune fencing can improve the appearance and environmental acceptability of built defences that might otherwise detract from the dune landscape.

All dune management schemes should observe the following guidelines to maximise the probability of success and minimise impacts on the natural and human environment:

- Each dune erosion site must be considered independently, with management approaches tailored to the specific site.
- A policy of "Adaptive management" (Summary 1) should be considered for all sites before other options are assessed.
- Work should not be undertaken unless the beach-dune system and nearshore coastal processes have been monitored over several years and a reasonable understanding of the physical and natural environment has been established. Hasty responses to erosion may prove to be either unnecessary or damaging.
- No work of a permanent nature should be undertaken unless important immovable or irreplaceable backshore assets are at risk.
- Local interest groups, such as landowners, nature trusts, fishing associations and recreational users, should be consulted early to ensure that a broad view of the shoreline and nearshore zone is considered prior to implementing any particular management approach.
- Consideration must always be given to both long term "average" and short term extreme weather and sea conditions to determine the life expectancy of any operations.
- Consideration must be given to the consequences of failure, such as construction debris spread along the beach, public safety hazards, loss of amenity access, deterioration of the landscape, etc.
- Work should be planned and scheduled to limit damage to fragile ecosystems and to recreation. Consideration should be given to vegetation, bird nesting and migration, intertidal invertebrates, fisheries, public access, noise levels and public safety.
- All site staff must be made aware of the need for careful working practises to avoid environmental damage, and to avoid hazards associated with steep and unstable dune faces.
- Temporary or permanent management access routes to the dune face for materials, equipment and labour must be planned and constructed to minimise trampling damage to the dunes and to limit the formation of blowouts. Boardwalks or other temporary surfaces should be laid and should follow the natural contours of the dunes rather than cutting straight lines susceptible to wind erosion. Fencing should be used to stabilise sand adjacent to the track.
- Public access routes to the beach should be clearly laid out and fenced where necessary to prevent trampling that may lead to blowouts.
- Educational displays at backshore car parking areas or along footpaths should be used to explain management schemes and encourage public interest and support for the management objectives.
- Warning signs should be set up highlighting the dangers of unstable dune faces, any construction work in progress or any other hazards associated with the management schemes (gaps in rock structures, slippery algal growth, buried defences, submerged structures, mud deposits, etc)
- Post project monitoring should be undertaken at least bi-annually to assess the beach-dune evolution and the success of the scheme relative to the objectives. Appendix 2 of this guide provides monitoring guidelines.

In addition to these general guidelines the following are of specific importance to dune grass planting:

- Further detailed guidance on transplanting is available from several publications including the BTCV "Sand Dunes Handbook" (1996).
- Transplants should only include those species that are indigenous to the site to maintain the natural ecosystem.
- Transplant schemes must be continuously managed to establish a vigorous growth and to repair natural or human damage.
- Re-profiling, thatching or fencing are normally required in association with planting to enhance dune recovery and to restrict public access or damage by stock.
- Transplanting should be undertaken in the spring to maximise potential growth and minimise the risk of storm erosion.

Summary 3: DUNE THATCHING

APPROPRIATE LOCATIONS	Above normal limit of wave run-up at any location with available blown sand. Unlikely to succeed where erosion is severe.
COSTS	Low, but labour intensive and requires ongoing maintenance. (£200 - £2000/100m length plus cost of transplanting and annual maintenance)
EFFECTIVENESS	Enhancement to natural dune recovery. Modest resistance to storm erosion. Enhanced by vegetation transplanting.
BENEFITS	Minimal impact on natural system. Materials are all natural, degradable and low cost.
PROBLEMS	Without maintenance thatching will last no more than 1 year. Materials are often used to build bonfires.

General description

Thatching of exposed dunes faces or blowouts using waste cuttings from forestry management, or other low cost materials, is a traditional way of stabilising sand, reducing trampling and protecting vegetation. Materials are low cost if locally available and no machinery or skilled labour is required to achieve success, but continual maintenance is important. The approach is normally carried out with dune grass planting to encourage dune stability. Thatching materials are often removed for bonfires by beach users.

Thatching and brushwood fencing along an eroded dune face.

Function

Well laid thatch will encourage dune recovery and will resist some erosion, but cannot prevent erosion where wave attack is frequent and damaging. The thatch reduces surface wind speeds, encouraging deposition of blown sand. Success depends on the amount of blown sand, the frequency of wave attack and the availability of vegetation. Transplanting dune grasses (Summary 2) after thatching will enhance dune recovery and longer term stability. Continual maintenance and replenishment of cuttings is required.

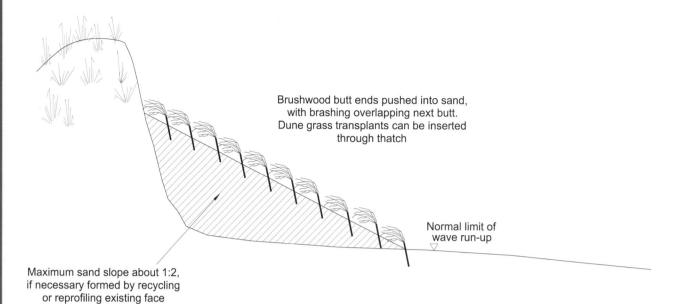

Brushwood butt ends pushed into sand,
with brashing overlapping next butt.
Dune grass transplants can be inserted
through thatch

Normal limit of
wave run-up
▽

Maximum sand slope about 1:2,
if necessary formed by recycling
or reprofiling existing face

Thatching an eroded dune face
Methods

Thatching has been practised for centuries and well established methods are presented in various publications, including the British Trust for Conservation Volunteers "Sand Dunes Handbook". Materials can include any form of timber or brushwood cuttings, although conifer brashings (lower branches) from spruce or fir are preferred for their flat, fan shapes. Thorny species, such as sea buckthorn (Hippophae rhamnoides), have the advantage of discouraging trampling and they are hard to burn, but can be highly invasive if cuttings or seeds become established as new growth. Thatch should be laid to cover 20% - 30% of the exposed sand surface. Dune grasses should be transplanted through the thatch to promote sand retention and restoration of natural habitats (Summary 2). Where public pressure is significant, access routes should be left between the beach and backshore, and fencing may be required to further protect slopes (Summary 4).

A similar effect can be achieved by mulching the dune face with coarse vegetative matter such as straw, seaweed or reeds. Transplants can be introduced through the mulch. This approach may not be appropriate for areas with very strong winds as the material may blow away. Mulching also brings concerns over introducing foreign plant seeds to the dune ecology, but has the advantage of increasing the organic content and water retention of the dune sand.

Biodegradable mats (jute or similar natural fibres) can be laid over the surface and pinned down. Transplants can be introduced through holes. However, mats are not usually recommended for marine erosion sites as they are likely to be disturbed by waves and left partly attached to the dune face where they will be unattractive and ineffective.

Thatching should not be undertaken on steep, freshly eroded slopes. The dune face should be regraded or built out with recycled sand (Summary 5) prior to further works. A maximum slope of 1:2 is recommended.

Thatching will be quickly damaged by wave action and should not extend seaward of the line of normal wave run-up. The approximate limit of wave run-up can be established by observing and recording the location of the strand line over Spring tide periods during both winter storms and more normal wave conditions. The toe of a freshly eroded dune face is normally at the run-up limit of the most recent severe sea.

Thatching requires regular maintenance to repair damage caused by erosion or the public, and to extend coverage as the dune system evolves. Work can be undertaken at any time of year, unless combined with transplanting when the spring is preferred. On exposed shorelines thatching may be completely lost during storms.

Costs for thatching are dependent on labour, material sources, extent of works, the need for ongoing management and the cost of ancillary works to help stabilise the dune face. Small schemes using volunteer labour and free brushwood will be very low cost. Larger schemes undertaken by contractors with large volumes of brushwood transported to site may cost up to £20,000/km, plus ongoing management costs. Cost assessments should allow for the possibility that dune thatching may be substantially damaged by the first storm event following works.

Rough thatching along an eroding machair edge, using local forestry cuttings.

Impacts

Thatching limits public access to the dunes and beach, and alters the appearance of the dune face. Blown litter and strand line debris can become trapped. The thatch material may introduce unwanted seeds or live cuttings to the dune ecology. Regular maintenance and provision of controlled access routes will minimise adverse public reaction to the visual impact and loss of recreational areas.

Best practice and environmental opportunities

Public access through the dunes and trampling of vegetation can be controlled at low cost by thatching. Wastage from forestry operations, roadside tree clearing and discarded Christmas trees can be used beneficially. Associated dune grass planting will help to stabilise the foredunes and will extend the dune habitat. Thatching is low cost and materials are degradable so failure will not jeopardise long term environmental interests.

All dune management schemes should observe the following guidelines to maximise the probability of success and minimise impacts on the natural and human environment:

- Each dune erosion site must be considered independently, with management approaches tailored to the specific site.
- A policy of "Adaptive management" (Summary 1) should be considered for all sites before other options are assessed.
- Work should not be undertaken unless the beach-dune system and nearshore coastal processes have been monitored over several years and a reasonable understanding of the physical and natural environment has been established. Hasty responses to erosion may prove to be either unnecessary or damaging.
- No work of a permanent nature should be undertaken unless important immovable or irreplaceable backshore assets are at risk.
- Local interest groups, such as landowners, nature trusts, fishing associations and recreational users, should be consulted early to ensure that a broad view of the shoreline and nearshore zone is considered prior to implementing any particular management approach.
- Consideration must always be given to both long term "average" and short term extreme weather and sea conditions to determine the life expectancy of any operations.
- Consideration must be given to the consequences of failure, such as construction debris spread along the beach, public safety hazards, loss of amenity access, deterioration of the landscape, etc.
- Work should be planned and scheduled to limit damage to fragile ecosystems and to recreation. Consideration should be given to vegetation, bird nesting and migration, intertidal invertebrates, fisheries, public access, noise levels and public safety.
- All site staff must be made aware of the need for careful working practises to avoid environmental damage, and to avoid hazards associated with steep and unstable dune faces.
- Temporary or permanent management access routes to the dune face for materials, equipment and labour must be planned and constructed to minimise trampling damage to the dunes and to limit the formation of blowouts. Boardwalks or other temporary surfaces should be laid and should follow the natural contours of the dunes rather than cutting straight lines susceptible to wind erosion. Fencing should be used to stabilise sand adjacent to the track.

- Public access routes to the beach should be clearly laid out and fenced where necessary to prevent trampling that may lead to blowouts.
- Educational displays at backshore car parking areas or along footpaths should be used to explain management schemes and encourage public interest and support for the management objectives.
- Warning signs should be set up highlighting the dangers of unstable dune faces, any construction work in progress or any other hazards associated with the management schemes (gaps in rock structures, slippery algal growth, buried defences, submerged structures, mud deposits, etc)
- Post project monitoring should be undertaken at least bi-annually to assess the beach-dune evolution and the success of the scheme relative to the objectives. Appendix 2 of this guide provides monitoring guidelines.

In addition to these general guidelines the following are of specific importance to dune thatching:

- Further detailed guidance on dune thatching is available from several publications including the BTCV "Sand Dunes Handbook".
- Thatch must be regularly maintained to maximise effectiveness and to minimise impact on public use and visual amenity.
- Materials must be degradable and should not introduce foreign seeds, live cuttings or pollutants that may damage the dune ecology. Sea buckthorn is a particularly invasive species and should be avoided as a thatch material if there are specific concerns about maintaining the local dune species distribution.
- Attention should be paid to areas suffering wind erosion as well as wave attack in order to prevent the formation of large blowouts.
- Vegetation transplanting will encourage dune growth and enhance the shoreline environment. Thatching without transplanting will have a short term impact only as any accumulated sand will remain unstable.

Summary 4: DUNE FENCING

Appropriate locations	Above normal limit of wave run-up at any location with available blown sand. Unlikely to succeed where erosion is severe.
Cost	Low, but requires on-going maintenance. (£400 - £2000/100m frontage length, plus cost of transplanting and on-going repairs)
Effectiveness	Enhancement to natural dune recovery. Limited resistance to storm erosion. Enhanced by vegetation transplanting.
Benefits	Minimal impact on natural system. Can be used to control public access and to improve other systems.
Problems	Damaged fences and accumulated debris can be unsightly. Fences need regular maintenance and have a maximum life of about 5 years depending on material, frequency of storm wave damage and vandalism.

General description

Construction of semi-permeable fences along the seaward face of dunes will encourage the deposition of wind blown sand, reduce trampling and protect existing or transplanted vegetation. A variety of fencing materials can be used successfully to enhance natural recovery. Fencing can also be used in conjunction with other management schemes to encourage dune stabilisation and reduce environmental impacts.

Dune fencing along upper beach.

Function

Sand fences cannot prevent erosion where wave attack is both frequent and damaging, but they will encourage foredune growth and resist some erosion. Fences reduce wind speed across the sand surface and encourage foredune deposition. They also act as a modest barrier to wave attack, reducing the erosion potential of waves near the limit of uprush.

Success depends on the void to solid ratio of the fence, the availability of blown sand, the frequency of wave attack at the fence and the amount of vegetation available to stabilise the accumulated sand. Success will be enhanced by a programme of dune grass transplanting (Summary 2), thatching (Summary 3) and beach recycling/regrading (Summary 5) to establish new foredunes.

Fencing and associated works can be used to enhance the appearance and effectiveness of other erosion defences. Rock, timber or gabion structures can provide a fixed line of defence, but are incongruous along a natural dune coast: partial burial by recycled or sand accreted by fencing and grasses will create a more natural dune environment.

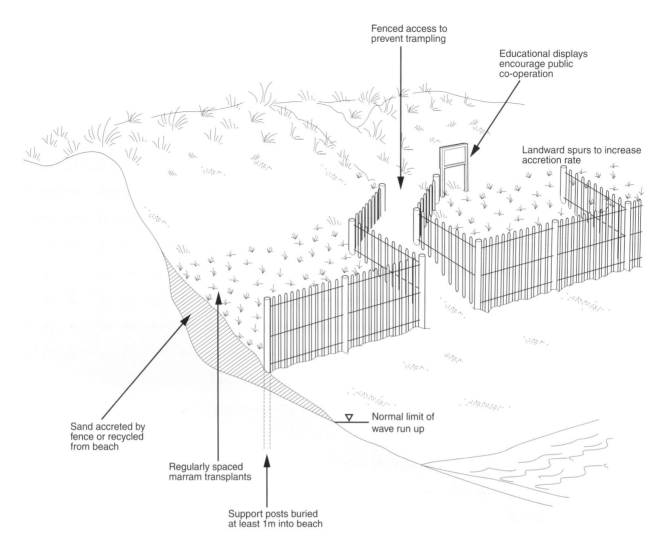

Fenced access to
prevent trampling

Educational displays
encourage public
co-operation

Landward spurs to increase
accretion rate

Sand accreted by
fence or recycled
from beach

Regularly spaced
marram transplants

Normal limit of
wave run up

Support posts buried
at least 1m into beach

Fencing used to stabilise an eroded dune face

Methods

Dune fencing to control wind erosion and encourage dune stability has been undertaken over many centuries, and the methods are covered in various publications, including the British Trust for Conservation Volunteers "Sand Dunes Handbook". Much the same methods are applicable to the management of marine erosion. Fencing materials can include chestnut palings, brushwood, wooden slats or synthetic fabrics. To be effective a void: solid ratio of 30% to 50% is required. Choice of materials will depend on required life, length of frontage commitment to maintenance and potential for vandalism.

Brushwood is normally the cheapest material, depending on labour costs, but has a life expectancy of no more than one year, assuming that it does not get removed for firewood. Synthetics vary from low cost materials such as strawberry netting up to expensive polyproplylene, nylon or composite wire/synthetic webs. Life expectancies of synthetics vary from one year to decades, and maintenance is minimal. Chestnut paling fencing is commonly used for dune management as it is widely available, easy to erect and has a life expectancy of 2-5 years. It should be noted that the standard paling fences used around construction sites have a void ratio well in excess of 50% and should not be used for dune management (see photograph below). Wooden slat fences are generally not recommended as they are prone to vandalism and are costly to erect. If used the slats should be not more than 50mm wide with gaps of the same size; wider slats will encourage local scour rather than deposition, and wider gaps will reduce efficiency in causing deposition.

Fencing can be installed forward of the toe of the dunes where it will be subject to occasional wave attack during storms. Low cost fence material, such as brushwood, can be considered expendable during very extreme events, but the posts and tensioning wires are best set up to last for several years at least as they are costly to replace. Posts should be long enough to allow burial to about 1m below the lowest expected beach level. At locations exposed to regular wave attack it may be necessary to place substantial timbers (e.g. railway sleepers) as posts to avoid annual reconstruction.

The approximate limits of wave run-up can be established by observing and recording the location of the strand line over Spring tide periods during both winter storms and more normal wave conditions. The toe of a freshly eroded dune face is normally at the run-up limit of the most recent severe sea.

Fencing should be set up parallel to the dune face, as no significant benefits have been found from attempting to orientate fences normal to the dominant wind. Short spurs running landward up the dune face can be beneficial to recovery in areas subject to dominant winds blowing at an acute angle to the shoreline. Spurs running seaward are less useful as they are likely to be damaged by swash zone debris or by beach users trying to walk along the shore at high tide.

Dune grass transplanting (Summary 2) should be undertaken after fencing, rather than before, to reduce trampling and to take full advantage of sand accumulated by the fencing. Successful sand fences may be buried within several seasons and a new line of fencing can be added to allow further foredune deposition. Fencing can be undertaken at any time of year, but associated transplanting is best completed in the spring.

Access routes to popular public beaches should be defined by the fencing at regular intervals (say 100m) along the dune face. Poorly planned access routes will encourage the public to damage fences in order to create their own paths.

It is possible to remove fencing for part of the year and to replace it again, though this may have little benefit and the extra work may be damaging to the dunes. Reasons for this may be to allow greater public access to the beach by removing fences in the summer, or to reduce potential damage to the fencing by winter storms. Either way, it will be necessary to place large, well bedded posts that can be left permanently in place when the fencing material is removed and stored.

Fencing costs vary according to labour, type of material used, quality, length and spacing of posts, frequency of spurs, frequency of public access points, need for management and the cost of ancillary works. Small schemes in low risk areas that are implemented by volunteers may cost less than £500/100m frontage. Contracted schemes involving fenced access routes, spurs and substantial straining piles may push costs up to £20,000/km, plus ongoing maintenance. Well constructed fences in appropriate locations should have a 5 year life.

Impacts

Sand fences limit public access to the dunes and beach, and can be visually intrusive. Fencing may accumulate blown litter or strand line debris, while damaged fences may interfere with the amenity use of the beach. Paling or slat fencing combine biodegradable timber with much longer lasting wire that may cause a long term nuisance. Synthetics are generally intended to be resistant to degradation and may remain as an unsightly part of the dune landscape for many years.

Best practice and environmental opportunities

Fencing along the dune toe allows public access to be controlled and reduces trampling of vegetation along the seaward edge of the dunes. Fencing and associated vegetation transplanting can help to stabilise the foredunes and will extend the dune habitat. They can also improve the appearance of other forms of built defences that might otherwise detract from the coastal landscape.

All dune management schemes should observe the following guidelines to maximise the probability of success and minimise impacts on the natural and human environment:

- Each dune erosion site must be considered independently, with management approaches tailored to the specific site.
- A policy of "Adaptive management" (Summary 1) should be considered for all sites before other options are assessed.
- Work should not be undertaken unless the beach-dune system and nearshore coastal processes have been monitored over several years and a reasonable understanding of the physical and natural environment has been established. Hasty responses to erosion may prove to be either unnecessary or damaging.
- No work of a permanent nature should be undertaken unless important immovable or irreplaceable backshore assets are at risk.
- Local interest groups, such as landowners, nature trusts, fishing associations and recreational users, should be consulted early to ensure that a broad view of the shoreline and nearshore zone is considered prior to implementing any particular management approach.
- Consideration must always be given to both long term "average" and short term extreme weather and sea conditions to determine the life expectancy of any operations.
- Consideration must be given to the consequences of failure, such as construction debris spread along the beach, public safety hazards, loss of amenity access, deterioration of the landscape, etc.
- Work should be planned and scheduled to limit damage to fragile ecosystems and to recreation. Consideration should be given to vegetation, bird nesting and migration, intertidal invertebrates, fisheries, public access, noise levels and public safety.
- All site staff must be made aware of the need for careful working practises to avoid environmental damage, and to avoid hazards associated with steep and unstable dune faces.
- Temporary or permanent management access routes to the dune face for materials, equipment and labour must be planned and constructed to minimise trampling damage to the dunes and to limit the formation of blowouts. Boardwalks or other temporary surfaces should be laid and should follow the natural contours of the dunes rather than cutting straight lines susceptible to wind erosion. Fencing should be used to stabilise sand adjacent to the track.
- Public access routes to the beach should be clearly laid out and fenced where necessary to prevent trampling that may lead to blowouts.
- Educational displays at backshore car parking areas or along footpaths should be used to explain management schemes and encourage public interest and support for the management objectives.
- Warning signs should be set up highlighting the dangers of unstable dune faces, any construction work in progress or any other hazards associated with the management schemes (gaps in rock structures, slippery algal growth, buried defences, submerged structures, mud deposits, etc)
- Post project monitoring should be undertaken at least bi-annually to assess the beach-dune evolution and the success of the scheme relative to the objectives. Appendix 2 of this guide provides monitoring guidelines.

In addition to these general guidelines, the following are of specific importance to dune fencing:

- Further detailed guidance on dune fencing is available from several publications including the BTCV "Sand Dunes Handbook".
- Synthetic fencing in bright colours should be avoided to minimise visual impact on the landscape.
- Non-degradable synthetic materials should be avoided in areas likely to be heavily affected by storms, as any material carried away by waves may become a hazard to swimmers, navigation and sealife.
- Regular maintenance should be undertaken to repair fencing and remove rotting or unsightly debris that may be caught along the fencing.
- The void to solid ratio for any fence material should be between 30% and 50% to achieve effective sand accumulation.
- Vegetation transplanting will encourage dune growth and enhance the shoreline environment. Fencing without transplanting will have a short term impact only as any accumulated sand will remain unstable.

Summary 5: BEACH RECYCLING AND REPROFILING

APPROPRIATE LOCATIONS	All locations, including those with limited blown sand for natural recovery.
COSTS	Low to moderate, but requires ongoing maintenance (£1000- £20,000 /100m length plus fencing, transplanting, etc, with similar repeat costs).
EFFECTIVENESS	Short term defence against erosion, and enhancement of natural recovery. Moderate resistance to single storms. Enhanced by fencing and vegetation transplanting, and can be successfully used to bury hard defences.
BENEFITS	Accelerates natural recovery of foredunes and provides short term defence against single severe storms.
PROBLEMS	Removes material from other sites, possibly transferring erosion or environmental damage to a different frontage. May introduce beach debris, non-indigenous sediment and/or vegetation, potentially damaging local ecology.

General description

Recycling is the mechanical shifting of sand, shingle or even boulders from an area of accretion to an area of erosion. Normally recycling would be undertaken at a local level, with sediment being taken from an accreting ridge, the lower beach or an estuary bar, and transported a short distance to an eroding dune face or a blow out. Alternatively the donor area may be to landward if sand is blown onto roads or other areas where it is not wanted and from where it can be recovered.

Reprofiling is an alternative term, usually referring to the direct transfer of material from the lower to the upper beach or, occasionally, the transfer of sand down the dune face from crest to toe.

If large structures, such as harbour breakwaters or river training walls, cross the beach then sediment may accumulate on the updrift side. This material can either be returned to the beach in the updrift direction, or can be mechanically bypassed around the structure to feed a downdrift beach.

Recycling sand or shingle can be undertaken to repair minor erosion problems such as blowouts, or it can be used to rebuild long lengths of upper beach. Use of boulders is usually restricted to relocating small numbers up the beach face to provide temporary armouring of a short length of dune face suffering minor erosion.

If material is imported from a source not related to the eroding site the approach is known as beach nourishment or recharging (Summary 7).

Reprofiled dune face following storm erosion. Sand taken from inter-tidal bar formed after storm event.

Function

Recycling provides an artificial buffer between the dune face and the erosive forces of the sea. Where erosion is active this buffer provides a short-term defence of the dunes, possibly only lasting through a single storm. Where the beach is stable or recovering, recycling accelerates the development of new foredunes. The success of this approach will be enhanced if combined with vegetation transplanting (Summary 2) and dune thatching (Summary 3) or fencing (Summary 4).

Recycling can also be used to enhance the coastal landscape by burying hard defences (sand bags, rock, gabions or timber), with the understanding that those defences may become re-exposed and active during storms. This will only be successful if the defences are high on the beach face - structures within the normally active foreshore zone will not be successfully buried as waves will rapidly remove the recycled material.

Methods

Recycling should only be undertaken where the shoreline manager has a good knowledge of local processes and beach movements developed from measurements and observations over at least several years. Sand or gravel should be sourced from areas known to be accreting, and scraping should not remove sufficient material to create a new erosion problem or to cause any significant environmental damage.

Relocating boulders from the foreshore to the dune toe may be an option for minor erosion problems, but the boulders will only provide a temporary defence against minor storm events, unless they are placed in sufficient quantity as a properly engineered rock revetment (Summary 14). Removal of rocks from the foreshore may well be damaging to local intertidal habitats, and will make an unattractive and largely ineffective addition to the dune face.

Prior to planning a beach recycling operation the ownership of the donor area must be established and appropriate consents sought. The intertidal area may be owned by the Crown Estates, a private estate, the Local Authority, the National Trust or other organisations.

Approx. 1m above maximum wave run-up level

Maximum 1:4 slope (sand can be extended at a flatter slope across upper beach)

Recycled sand or gravel

Recycled sand should be stabilised by transplanting, fencing and/or thatching

Recycled sand or gravel placed along an eroding dune face

The recycled material should be as similar as possible to the indigenous sediment. Sediment size, grading, shell content and material should match the upper beach and dune face. The material should also be clean and free of seeds. If these conditions are not met then the nourishment may cause unwanted changes to the beach and dune profiles, to the dune ecology and the dune appearance. Coarser sediments can be used, and may be more stable, but they are likely to cause the beach gradient to increase and will be less likely to form new foredunes. Ideally, environmental and hydraulic assessments should be carried out to determine the acceptability of sediments that do not meet the optimal criteria.

Scraping from a lower beach bar directly to seaward of an eroding dune face may well exacerbate existing problems. The bar will normally be a transient feature that acts to reduce wave attack by causing waves to break or refract before they reach the dune face. Any scraping should only remove a surface layer, say 200mm in depth.

Extraction may also be from other accreting areas, such as dunes, upper beach ridges or from estuary bars. Whatever the source it is important that the operation will not create a new erosion problem or habitat damage, and that the recycled material is acceptable in terms of environmental impact, hydraulic performance and appearance. Careful management should ensure that the donor site remains an area of net accretion into the future.

There is some debate as to the most effective position to place recycled sediment to achieve optimum protection. Possible locations include the upper beach and dune face, the mid to lower beach and the shallow nearshore zone. The former is most obvious as the benefits of recycling are immediate, but, if the sediment is primarily sand, it will be rapidly redistributed alongshore or across the beach face by waves and currents to form a new equilibrium profile (shingle tends to remain on the upper beach, but may be redistributed alongshore). Placement on the mid-beach anticipates this redistribution, and provides shoreline protection by helping to dissipate wave energy before it reaches the dunes. Placement below the water line also anticipates the redistribution and allows sand to be fed into the beach system gradually; this approach is more applicable to very large recharge schemes and is unlikely to be considered for dune management.

Although there is some merit in the alternative locations it is generally considered appropriate that deposition of the recycled material should be along the upper beach, above the high water line and along the eroding dune face. Natural redistribution of the placed material alongshore and cross-shore will occur, particularly for sand. Recycling operations should anticipate this redistribution by ensuring that the volume deposited to the upper beach is in excess of the amount required for immediate protection to the dune. The above figure provides some rough guidance as to appropriate beach profiles that will allow for continued erosion, but each site should be assessed separately. Consideration should be given to the past rates of erosion, the likely rate of redistribution and the intended life of the recycled material before the next recycling operation will be required. Fencing or thatching of the new dune line, followed by vegetation transplanting should enhance the success of the recycling operation (Summaries 2, 3 and 4). Ongoing management will allow the future recycling to be fine tuned for each site.

Recycling gravel can be very effective. A ridge of shingle along the dune face can provide good protection from wave erosion. The gravel may well be partially covered by sand during natural recovery, and may only be exposed by storms. A gravel ridge can be successfully controlled by groynes (Summary 10), although great care must be taken with design of these.

The approximate limits of wave run-up can be established by observing and recording the location of the strand line over Spring tide periods during both winter storms and more normal wave conditions. The toe of a freshly eroded dune face is normally at the run-up limit of the most recent severe sea.

Prior to placing recycled material along the dune face it may be prudent to remove some of the existing foredune vegetation for later transplanting. Vegetation buried by imported shingle or wet sand to a depth of more than a few centimetres may not recover.

Work can either be carried out as an emergency operation immediately after a storm to reduce the risk of follow on erosion, or as a planned maintenance operation in the spring. Maintenance work at this time will provide the greatest benefit to beach users over the summer and will maximise the length of time for establishing vegetation to stabilise the dunes. It is likely that recycling will have to be repeated annually or after severe erosion events.

The dimensions suggested by the accompanying sketch are basic minimums to serve as a guide for small recycling schemes. Greater and longer term success can be achieved by increasing volumes and by undertaking regular top-ups to maintain effective erosion protection. Large schemes should be designed by competent coastal consultants, following preliminary studies of the physical, natural and human environment.

Equipment required varies with the size of the scheme and the duration of the work. A small wheel loader and several dump trucks are suitable for moving a few hundred cubic metres over a couple of days, but recycling larger volumes over several miles of beach will require heavy earth moving equipment.

Mechanical cleaning occurs along some busy public beaches. This process removes some sand along with litter and strand line debris. Simple screening can separate most of the sand allowing it to be placed beneficially back on the upper beach without the debris, which should be disposed of properly.

Costs for recycling vary widely, depending on the scheme objectives, volumes, distances of transport, frequency of ongoing works and the need for beach control structures such as groynes or breakwaters. Minor works to repair blowouts may cost only a few hundred pounds, while large scale works may run to £200,000/km and may need to be repeated annually. Control structures will reduce ongoing maintenance costs but will greatly increase initial construction costs.

Impacts

Sand deposited on the upper beach may be subject to wind erosion, causing an unwanted increase in blown sand across the back shore; fencing and vegetation transplanting will reduce this problem. The deposits may also bury existing vegetation and intertidal invertebrate communities, reducing the natural stability of the foredunes and destroying habitats. As a general rule impacts will be less for regular, small recycling operations than for occasional large operations.

Scraping from the source area may allow erosion of a new area of shoreline. If the source is within an estuary the response to extensive scraping may be difficult to predict, and erosion problems may appear at some distance away.

Layer of wind-blown sand upon reprofiled dune face. Sand retention and accumulation has been encouraged by re-planting of the reprofiled slope.

Extraction from the source area may also cause local damage to habitats, land forms or amenity. Intertidal scraping or boulder removal is likely to disturb benthic communities, while re-profiling the dune crest will largely destroy the local dune habitat, landform and landscape.

If the source material contains dissimilar sediments relative to the indigenous dune sand (e.g. boulders, gravels or estuary silt), beach debris, or vegetation/seeds that are foreign to the dune system, the dune geomorphology and ecology may be adversely affected. Any fine materials will be washed out of the recycled beach, potentially damaging nearshore fisheries and benthic communities.

Best practice and environmental opportunities

Recycling will enhance the natural recovery of dune face erosion and provide a wider recreational beach. The initial artificial appearance of the upper beach and dune face will quickly be transformed by wind, waves and vegetation to a more natural form. Recycling can be combined with fencing, thatching and transplanting to encourage development of new foredunes and an extended dune habitat. Hard defences built high on the beach face can be buried by recycled material, followed by fencing and transplanting, to create a much more natural shoreline.

All dune management schemes should observe the following guidelines to maximise the probability of success and minimise impacts on the natural and human environment:

● Each dune erosion site must be considered independently, with management approaches tailored to the specific site.

● A policy of "Adaptive management" (Summary 1) should be considered for all sites before other options are assessed.

● Work should not be undertaken unless the beach-dune system and nearshore coastal processes have been monitored over several years and a reasonable understanding of the physical and natural environment has been established. Hasty responses to erosion may prove to be either unnecessary or damaging.

● No work of a permanent nature should be undertaken unless important immovable or irreplaceable backshore assets are at risk.

● Local interest groups, such as landowners, nature trusts, fishing associations and recreational users, should be consulted early to ensure that a broad view of the shoreline and nearshore zone is considered prior to implementing any particular management approach.

- Consideration must always be given to both long term "average" and short term extreme weather and sea conditions to determine the life expectancy of any operations.
- Consideration must be given to the consequences of failure, such as construction debris spread along the beach, public safety hazards, loss of amenity access, deterioration of the landscape, etc.
- Work should be planned and scheduled to limit damage to fragile ecosystems and to recreation. Consideration should be given to vegetation, bird nesting and migration, intertidal invertebrates, fisheries, public access, noise levels and public safety.
- All site staff must be made aware of the need for careful working practises to avoid environmental damage, and to avoid hazards associated with steep and unstable dune faces.
- Temporary or permanent management access routes to the dune face for materials, equipment and labour must be planned and constructed to minimise trampling damage to the dunes and to limit the formation of blowouts. Boardwalks or other temporary surfaces should be laid and should follow the natural contours of the dunes rather than cutting straight lines susceptible to wind erosion. Fencing should be used to stabilise sand adjacent to the track.
- Public access routes to the beach should be clearly laid out and fenced where necessary to prevent trampling that may lead to blowouts.
- Educational displays at backshore car parking areas or along footpaths should be used to explain management schemes and encourage public interest and support for the management objectives.
- Warning signs should be set up highlighting the dangers of unstable dune faces, any construction work in progress or any other hazards associated with the management schemes (gaps in rock structures, slippery algal growth, buried defences, submerged structures, mud deposits, etc)
- Post project monitoring should be undertaken at least bi-annually to assess the beach-dune evolution and the success of the scheme relative to the objectives. Appendix 2 of this guide provides monitoring guidelines.

In addition to these general guidelines the following are of specific importance to beach recycling:

- Large scale recycling schemes should be designed by a competent coastal consultant following preliminary shoreline management studies
- Further guidance on recycling is available from the CIRIA "Beach Management Manual".
- Careful consideration must be given to the long-term management commitment required to establish and maintain an adequate level of erosion protection. Future funding of monitoring and regular top-ups should be agreed before considering this option.
- Both the donor and receptor sites should be monitored before and after recycling to determine the impact and success of the operation. Profile surveys should be repeated at least twice each year along fixed cross-shore lines.
- Extraction of sand or shingle from the upper beach should not be allowed to damage existing dune vegetation in the source area.
- Deposits may smother intertidal benthic communities, disrupting the local ecology. Obvious consequences will include the temporary loss of feeding grounds for waders. Careful consideration must be given to this potential impact.
- Fine silts imported with the nourishment material will be gradually washed out, potentially causing short-term damage to nearshore fisheries and benthic communities. Again, careful consideration must be given to this impact and particularly to the timing of works in relation to fisheries.
- Any material taken from the backshore or from within an estuary should be checked for debris, pollutants and non-indigenous plant material prior to being transported to the deposition area.
- Recycled sand will be subject to wind erosion, so should be stabilised by vegetation transplanting and fencing.
- Rock or timber revetments can be buried with sand or shingle, but gabions and sand bags should only be buried by sand to avoid abrasion damage. Burial should be accompanied by fencing and transplanting to encourage stable new dunes to develop.

Summary 6:   SAND BAG STRUCTURES

APPROPRIATE LOCATIONS	Low to moderate energy sandy shorelines requiring lower cost, temporary defence.
COSTS	Low to moderate (£2,000-£10,000/100m frontage)
EFFECTIVENESS	Provides short term fixed line of defence. Less than 5 year life. Burial may extend life.
BENEFITS	Low cost, low skill approach using local materials that are returned to the beach when the defences no longer required.
PROBLEMS	Sand bags subject to vandalism and rapid deterioration due to wave action, sunlight and public pressure. Bags are effectively impermeable and do not absorb wave energy, so beach scour may accelerate.

General description
Sand bags of various sizes and lengths can be used to form temporary reefs, breakwaters, groynes, headlands or revetments on sand beaches. Sturdy geotextile bags are filled in-situ with local beach sand and therefore have a relatively low cost.

Function
Sand bag structures can be placed without the need for costly equipment or skilled labour. They can be used to form any form of shoreline structure but will have a short life expectancy due to lack of resistance to physical damage (wave borne debris impacts or vandalism) and the effects of UV sunlight. They are potentially most useful as a buried revetment under the dune face, where they will form a final line of protection after the overlaying sand has been eroded by storm waves. An alternative use is to form temporary headlands (Summary 9) to protect backshore assets while other, longer term, options are planned and implemented.

Methods
Bags should be filled and closed according to manufacturer's recommendations. Care is required throughout to avoid selection should be governed by the anticipated methods of filling and placing on site. Labour intensive operations will limit bags to about 50kg and will only be appropriate for small schemes in low wave energy conditions. Large schemes will require filling and lifting equipment. A practical bag size limit is about 3m x 1.5m x 0.5m, containing about 3 tonnes of sand. Long tubes have been used in the past, but these are more likely to fail, as a single tear will affect the whole tube.

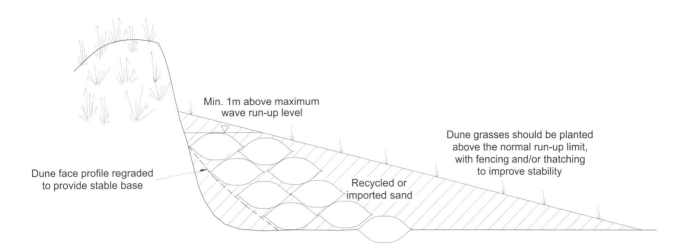

Min. 1m above maximum
wave run-up level

Dune grasses should be planted
above the normal run-up limit,
with fencing and/or thatching
to improve stability

Dune face profile regraded
to provide stable base

Recycled or
imported sand

Buried sand bag revetment acting as
final line of defence under recycled
or nourished sand beach. Details of
revetment depend on size of bag used and
expected exposure to storm waves

Buried sand bag revetment

Prior to construction the dune face will need to be dressed to form a plane slope on which bags can be laid evenly. This slope should not be steeper than 1:1.5. Sandbags should be stacked against the dune face, as shown on the enclosed sketch. The bags should be placed with their long axes parallel to the beach line. A minimum thickness of 2 bag widths is recommended, with a thickness of 3 bag widths for the lowest course to reduce scour. The seaward line of bags should be treated as sacrificial. The bags should be filled in-situ, by hand or by pumping in a slurry of sand and water. Fill material can be recycled or imported sand or fine gravel. The toe of the completed revetment should be landward of the limit of normal wave run-up to avoid scour problems. The crest should be about 1m above the limit of run-up during storms to avoid overtopping damage to the dune face.

The approximate limits of wave run-up can be established by observing and recording the location of the strand line over Spring tide periods during both winter storms and more normal wave conditions. The toe of a freshly eroded dune face is normally just below the run-up limit of the most recent severe sea.

Bags intended to provide a buried revetment as a final line of defence should be covered by recycled (Summary 5) or imported sand, stabilised by transplanted vegetation and fencing/thatching (Summaries 2, 3 and 4). If a good quality geotextile is used to make the bags, and if a regular recycling programme is maintained to make good seasonal erosion, then a life expectancy of 10 years might be assumed. More realistically sandbags will have a much more limited life expectancy, say 5 years at best.

Damage to sand bag structures will be most intense at the alongshore extremes due to displacement by wave action, local scouring of beach levels and vandalism/public pressure. The ends of exposed structures should be feathered smoothly back into the dune face with the last 5m-10m of bags buried by several metres to allow for some future erosion. Maintenance attention should be focused on these potential problem areas.

Costs depend mainly on labour, structure dimensions and the need to bury the sandbags. Small schemes can be undertaken with volunteer labour with a minimum of lifting equipment, while larger schemes will require contractors with heavy lifting, pumping and earth moving plant. Costs of up to £100,000/km can be expected, with an anticipated scheme life of no more than 5 years.

Impacts

Exposed sand bags are unsightly and easily damaged. As structures are effectively impermeable they will not absorb wave energy, and may cause local beach scour to accelerate. Damaged bags will release the fill material back onto the beach, but the bags will remain as unsightly debris along the shoreline. Assuming that the fill material is taken locally or is similar to the beach material then losses will be harmless.

As with all fixed defences the sand bags will interfere with the natural dynamic interchange of material between beach and dune. They will also influence the longshore transfer of sand, modify dune habitats, disrupt the natural landform and potentially result in localised dune face scour at their terminal ends.

Best practice and environmental opportunities

Buried sand bags can form a useful and low cost final line of defence in areas subject to mild, seasonal erosion. They are also useful for temporary (less than 5 years) headland protection while other options are considered, planned and implemented, but they should be superseded by a longer term solution. They have no environmental benefits except that they are temporary structures, easily removed with no significant long term impacts on the physical or natural environment.

All dune management schemes should observe the following guidelines to maximise the probability of success and minimise impacts on the natural and human environment:

- Each dune erosion site must be considered independently, with management approaches tailored to the specific site.
- A policy of "Adaptive management" (Summary 1) should be considered for all sites before other options are assessed.
- Work should not be undertaken unless the beach-dune system and nearshore coastal processes have been monitored over several years and a reasonable understanding of the physical and natural environment has been established. Hasty responses to erosion may prove to be either unnecessary or damaging.
- No work of a permanent nature should be undertaken unless important immovable or irreplaceable backshore assets are at risk.
- Local interest groups, such as landowners, nature trusts, fishing associations and recreational users, should be consulted early to ensure that a broad view of the shoreline and nearshore zone is considered prior to implementing any particular management approach.
- Consideration must always be given to both long term "average" and short term extreme weather and sea conditions to determine the life expectancy of any operations.
- Consideration must be given to the consequences of failure, such as construction debris spread along the beach, public safety hazards, loss of amenity access, deterioration of the landscape, etc.
- Work should be planned and scheduled to limit damage to fragile ecosystems and to recreation. Consideration should be given to vegetation, bird nesting and migration, intertidal invertebrates, fisheries, public access, noise levels and public safety.
- All site staff must be made aware of the need for careful working practises to avoid environmental damage, and to avoid hazards associated with steep and unstable dune faces.
- Temporary or permanent management access routes to the dune face for materials, equipment and labour must be planned and constructed to minimise trampling damage to the dunes and to limit the formation of blowouts. Boardwalks or other temporary surfaces should be laid and should follow the natural contours of the dunes rather than cutting straight lines susceptible to wind erosion. Fencing should be used to stabilise sand adjacent to the track.
- Public access routes to the beach should be clearly laid out and fenced where necessary to prevent trampling that may lead to blowouts.
- Educational displays at backshore car parking areas or along footpaths should be used to explain management schemes and encourage public interest and support for the management objectives.
- Warning signs should be set up highlighting the dangers of unstable dune faces, any construction work in progress or any other hazards associated with the management schemes (gaps in rock structures, slippery algal growth, buried defences, submerged structures, mud deposits, etc)
- Post project monitoring should be undertaken at least bi-annually to assess the beach-dune evolution and the success of the scheme relative to the objectives. Appendix 2 of this guide provides monitoring guidelines.

In addition to these general guidelines, the following are of specific importance to sand bag structures:

- Exposed sand bag structures are only appropriate for temporary protection while other management solutions are planned and implemented; buried structures have a somewhat longer life expectancy, and have less impact on habitat, landform and landscape.
- Damaged sandbags should be repaired rapidly to avoid failure of the structure, or removed to avoid any detriment to the landscape.
- Once the structures have served their intended short term function they should be removed to prevent landscape impacts and to allow natural processes to resume.
- Where possible recycling, fencing and transplanting should be undertaken to establish a new line of foredunes over the sandbags. Burial will increase the sand bag life, while the new dunes will enhance the coastal landscape, provide additional erosion protection and re-establish a natural succession of dune habitats from the shoreline to the backshore.

Summary 7: BEACH NOURISHMENT

APPROPRIATE LOCATIONS	High value amenity beaches. Shorelines suffering erosion due to updrift construction works or channel dredging. Mixed sand/gravel beaches with moderate to high value backshore assets.
COSTS	Moderate to high, and requires ongoing maintenance (£5,000-£200,000/100m frontage, plus control structures, ongoing management and minor works).
EFFECTIVENESS	Short to medium term reduction in erosion. Enhancement to natural recovery. 1 to 10 year life before first major recharge.
BENEFITS	Erosion protection without hard structures. Natural beach processes retained. Recreational value of beach enhanced.
PROBLEMS	Appropriate materials may be unavailable or expensive. Dissimilar imported material may alter geomorphology or ecology. Sand may be blown inland causing a nuisance.

General description

Beach nourishment (also known as beach recharging) involves the importing of sand or gravel to make good losses due to erosion. If the source of material is local and related by coastal processes to the eroding area then this approach is known as recycling (Summary 5). Nourishment schemes can vary from a few truckloads to repair a blow out or other small eroded area up to multi-million pound schemes requiring sea delivery of sand dredged from the seabed.

The beach at Portobello has been renourished with sand dredged from offshore.

Function

The imported material may be placed on the intertidal foreshore where it will help to protect the dunes by increasing wave energy dissipation across the beach. Alternatively the material may be placed directly at the dune face to form an artificial foredune.

Nourishment with sand is normally only appropriate to high value amenity beaches or small pocket beaches. The sand is quickly redistributed alongshore and offshore by waves, currents and winds, so large volumes and continuing top ups are required to achieve a lasting benefit. In areas with existing mixed sand/gravel beaches a gravel nourishment can be cost effective. The gravel tends to form a narrow storm ridge along the toe of the dunes from where it is redistributed alongshore by wave action at high tide only.

The success of a nourishment scheme will be enhanced by vegetation transplanting and fencing or thatching (Summaries 2, 3 and 4). In some instances the nourishment may also benefit from the construction of groynes, reefs, breakwaters or sills (Summaries 10, 11 and 12), that will reduce longshore transport losses. Where high value assets are to be protected, the nourishment scheme may be backed by a fixed line of defence such as a gabion or rock revetment (Summaries 8 and 14), possibly buried by the nourishment.

Method

Before giving serious consideration to this approach the dune manager should investigate potential sources of nourishment material. Appropriate materials in the required volumes may not be available at a cost that is acceptable. There are few licensed dredge areas around Scotland, and there is strong competition for both the material and for the dredge vessels. Alternatively materials may come from navigation maintenance dredging or onshore sites. Dredge spoil may be available from ports, but must be carefully sampled prior to use to ensure that materials do not contain too much mud, and that they are not contaminated in any way. Land based sources may be most suitable for small recharge schemes and for top ups, as start up costs are likely to be lower and materials are likely to be more readily available in small quantities. If material is available it may not conform to the ideal size or quality standards desired for the dune management site. Compromises are likely to be required.

Nourishment should only be undertaken where the shoreline manager has a good knowledge of local processes and beach movements, developed from measurements and observations over at least several years. Nourishment methods are dependent on the scale of operations. The Guide does not consider appropriate methods for nourishment schemes involving transfer of sediment from the sea; these larger scale operations are covered by the CIRIA Beach Management Manual and should be designed by competent consultants.

Delivery from land (whether port dredge spoil or quarried) will involve large numbers of vehicles using local roads, accessing the beach and placing the material. Each phase of this operation will have impacts on people and the natural environment. Work schedules will be controlled by the tide, and cost efficiency may demand night work or a schedule that is damaging to habitat. The significance of these issues will be site specific, but must be carefully considered. Delivery from the sea is less damaging, but cost effectiveness depends on the economies of scale and the source of the material.

Major renourishment operations typically require sand to be pumped onshore from dredgers

The nourishment material should be as similar as possible to the indigenous sediment. Sediment size, grading, shell content and material should match the upper beach and dune face. The material should also be clean and free of seeds. If these conditions are not met then the nourishment may cause unwanted changes to the beach and dune profiles, to the dune ecology and the dune appearance. Coarser sediments can be used, and may create a more stable upper beach, but they are likely to cause the beach gradient to increase and will be less likely to form new foredunes. Environmental and hydraulic assessments should be carried out to determine the acceptability of available sediments if they do meet the ideal criteria.

There is some debate as to the most effective position to place the nourishment to achieve optimum protection. Possible locations include the upper beach and dune face, the mid to lower beach and the shallow nearshore zone. The former is most obvious as the benefits of nourishment are immediate, but, if the sediment is primarily sand, it will be rapidly redistributed alongshore or across the beach face by waves and currents to form a new equilibrium profile (shingle tends to remain on the upper beach, but may be redistributed alongshore). Placement of sand on the mid-beach anticipates this redistribution, and provides shoreline protection by helping

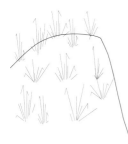

Approx. 1m above maximum wave run-up level

Maximum 1:4 slope (sand can be extended at a flatter slope across upper beach)

Imported sand or gravel

Imported sand should be stabilised by transplanting, fencing and/or thatching

Imported sand or gravel placed along an eroding dune face

to dissipate wave energy before it reaches the dunes. Placement below the water line also anticipates the redistribution and allows sand to be fed into the beach system gradually. This latter approach is only appropriate to very large recharge schemes and is unlikely to be considered for dune management.

Although there is some merit in the alternative locations it is generally considered appropriate that deposition of the nourishment material should be along the upper beach, above the high water line and along the eroding dune face. Natural redistribution of the placed material alongshore and cross-shore will occur, particularly for sand. Nourishment operations should anticipate this redistribution by ensuring that the volume deposited to the upper beach is in excess of the amount required for immediate protection to the dune. The above figure provides some rough guidance as to appropriate beach profiles that will allow for continued erosion, but each site should be assessed separately. Consideration should be given to the past rates of erosion, the likely rate of redistribution and the intended life of the nourishment before the next top-up operation will be required. Fencing or thatching of the new dune line, followed by vegetation transplanting should enhance the success of the recharge operation (Summaries 2, 3 and 4). Ongoing management will allow the future nourishment to be fine tuned for each site.

Nourishing with gravel can be very effective. A ridge of shingle along the dune face can provide good protection from wave erosion. The gravel may well be partially covered by sand during natural recovery, and may only be exposed by storms. A gravel ridge can be successfully controlled by groynes (Summary 10), although great care must be taken with design of these.

The approximate limits of wave run-up can be established by observing and recording the location of the strand line over Spring tide periods during both winter storms and more normal wave conditions. The toe of a freshly eroded dune face is normally at the run-up limit of the most recent severe sea.

Prior to placing material along the dune face it may be prudent to remove some of the existing vegetation for later transplanting. Vegetation buried by imported shingle or wet sand to a depth of more than a few centimetres may not recover.

Nourishment is most appropriate to pocket beaches where little material is lost from the system. On long, exposed beaches where longshore transport is likely to redistribute the nourishment material rapidly, there may be a need to provide beach control structures such as headlands, reefs, breakwaters or groynes. Attempting to control sand beaches in areas with high tidal ranges is unlikely to be successful unless massive cross-shore structures are used. Gravel ridges along the upper beach are much easier to control and require relatively small structures.

The dimensions suggested by the accompanying sketch are basic minimums to serve as a guide for small nourishment schemes. Greater and longer term success can be achieved by increasing volumes and by undertaking regular top-ups to maintain effective erosion protection. Large schemes should be designed by competent coastal consultants, following preliminary studies of the physical, natural and human environment.

Schemes are best implemented in the spring and early summer when work windows are least restricted and the nourishment has the greatest chance to stabilise before winter storms start to erode and redistribute the beach.

Costs for a nourishment scheme depend on the source of material, transport methods, volumes required, the need for beach control structures, (groynes, breakwaters etc.), the need for secondary defences, expected scheme life before topping-up and the amount of minor works undertaken to enhance the dune system. Small recharges using locally quarried gravel that is transported easily to site by road may cost as little as £5000/100m frontage. Schemes requiring large volumes of offshore dredged sand, pumped ashore from barges and requiring substantial top ups at, say, 5 yearly intervals may have an initial cost of £2,000,000/1km with ongoing management costs of £400,000 each year. If secondary defences or control structures are also included, the initial costs may rise to as much as £4,000,000/km but future management costs could drop to, say, £100,000/km each year.

Impacts

Sand deposited on the upper beach may be subject to wind erosion, causing an unwanted increase in blown sand across the back shore; fencing and vegetation transplanting will reduce this problem. The deposits may also bury existing vegetation and intertidal invertebrate communities, reducing the natural stability of the foredunes and destroying habitats. As a general rule impacts will be less for regular, small nourishment operations than for occasional large operations.

If the source material contains sediments dissimilar to the indigenous dune beach sand (e.g. gravels or estuary silt), or if it contains vegetation or seeds that are foreign to the dune system then the dune geomorphology and ecology may be adversely affected. Any fine materials will be washed out of the nourished beach, potentially impacting on nearshore fisheries and invertebrate communities.

Best practice and environmental opportunities

Nourishment will increase the volume of beach and/or dune material, and will enhance the natural recovery of dune face erosion. Where large volumes of material are imported, nourishment can provide a wide upper beach for recreational use, and will gradually feed sediment to adjacent beaches due to longshore drift. The initial artificial appearance of the upper beach and dune face will be quickly transformed by wind, waves and vegetation to a more natural form.

Nourishment can be combined with fencing, thatching and transplanting to encourage development of new foredunes and an extended dune habitat. Hard defences built high on the beach face can be buried by the nourishment, followed by fencing and transplanting, to create a much more natural shore.

All dune management schemes should observe the following guidelines to maximise the probability of success and minimise impacts on the natural and human environment:

- Each dune erosion site must be considered independently, with management approaches tailored to the specific site.
- A policy of "Adaptive management" (Summary 1) should be considered for all sites before other options are assessed.
- Work should not be undertaken unless the beach-dune system and nearshore coastal processes have been monitored over several years and a reasonable understanding of the physical and natural environment has been established. Hasty responses to erosion may prove to be either unnecessary or damaging.
- No work of a permanent nature should be undertaken unless important immovable or irreplaceable backshore assets are at risk.
- Local interest groups, such as landowners, nature trusts, fishing associations and recreational users, should be consulted early to ensure that a broad view of the shoreline and nearshore zone is considered prior to implementing any particular management approach.
- Consideration must always be given to both long term "average" and short term extreme weather and sea conditions to determine the life expectancy of any operations.
- Consideration must be given to the consequences of failure, such as construction debris spread along the beach, public safety hazards, loss of amenity access, deterioration of the landscape, etc.
- Work should be planned and scheduled to limit damage to fragile ecosystems and to recreation. Consideration should be given to vegetation, bird nesting and migration, intertidal invertebrates, fisheries, public access, noise levels and public safety.
- All site staff must be made aware of the need for careful working practises to avoid environmental damage, and to avoid hazards associated with steep and unstable dune faces.

- Temporary or permanent management access routes to the dune face for materials, equipment and labour must be planned and constructed to minimise trampling damage to the dunes and to limit the formation of blowouts. Boardwalks or other temporary surfaces should be laid and should follow the natural contours of the dunes rather than cutting straight lines susceptible to wind erosion. Fencing should be used to stabilise sand adjacent to the track.
- Public access routes to the beach should be clearly laid out and fenced where necessary to prevent trampling that may lead to blowouts.
- Educational displays at backshore car parking areas or along footpaths should be used to explain management schemes and encourage public interest and support for the management objectives.
- Warning signs should be set up highlighting the dangers of unstable dune faces, any construction work in progress or any other hazards associated with the management schemes (gaps in rock structures, slippery algal growth, buried defences, submerged structures, mud deposits, etc)
- Post project monitoring should be undertaken at least bi-annually to assess the beach-dune evolution and the success of the scheme relative to the objectives. Appendix 2 of this guide provides monitoring guidelines.

In addition to these general guidelines, the following are of specific importance to beach nourishment:

- Large scale nourishment schemes should be designed by a competent coastal consultant following preliminary shoreline management studies and detailed consideration of all other options.
- Further guidance on beach nourishment is available from the CIRIA "Beach Management Manual".
- Careful consideration must be given to the long-term management commitment required to establish and maintain an adequate level of erosion protection. Future funding of monitoring and regular top-ups should be agreed before considering this option.
- Beaches formed of dredged shingle may erode back to form small "cliffs" at the limit of wave uprush. These can be hazardous to beach users and should be regraded on popular public beaches.
- Nourishment may smother intertidal benthic communities, disrupting the local ecology. Obvious consequences will include the temporary loss of feeding grounds for waders. Careful consideration must be given to this potential impact.
- Fine silts imported with the nourishment material will be gradually washed out, potentially causing short-term damage to nearshore fisheries and benthic communities. Again, careful consideration must be given to this impact and particularly to the timing of works in relation to fisheries.
- Nourishment sites should be monitored before and after operations to determine the impact and success. Profiles should be repeated at least twice a year along fixed cross-shore lines.
- Sand deposits will be subject to wind erosion and redistribution, so should be stabilised by transplanting and fencing. Failure to stabilise the foredunes may result in problems over wind blown sand across the backshore.
- Rock or timber revetments can be buried with sand or shingle, but gabions and sand bags should only be buried by sand to avoid abrasion damage. Burial should be accompanied by fencing and transplanting to encourage stable new foredunes to develop.

APPROPRIATE LOCATIONS	Sandy beach sites suffering periodic moderate to severe erosion where backshore assets are at risk. Useful for estuary bank protection.
COSTS	Moderate, but require maintenance (£5000-£50,000/100m of frontage, plus minor works and maintenance).
EFFECTIVENESS	Well placed gabions provide reasonable fixed defences, but have a limited life of 5-10 years due to deterioration of the baskets.
BENEFITS	Useful solution where armour rock is considered inappropriate or too costly. Various forms available. Can be buried by sand and vegetation. Permeable face absorbs wave energy and encourages upper beach stability.
PROBLEMS	Limited life, leading to unsightly and hazardous wire baskets along beach and the release of non-indigenous cobbles to the beach system. Wire affected by saltwater, vandalism and abrasion by trampling or gravel beach impacts.

General description

Gabions are wire mesh baskets filled with cobbles or crushed rock. They are filled insitu, often with locally available material and therefore have a relatively low capital cost. Because they are flexible and porous they can absorb some wave and wind energy, thereby reducing the scour problems associated with impermeable sea defences such as concrete seawalls. Gabions can be placed as sloping "mattresses" or as near vertical cubic baskets. The latter are intended for bank or cliff stabilisation and are not normally suitable for use in shoreline situations.

Gabion revetments (foregound) are generally preferred to gabion walls (background) in coastal environments being less reflective of wave energy and more stable. Blown sand is also better able to accumulate on revetments, potentially softening their appearance.

74

Function

The purpose of a gabion revetment is to provide short term (5-10 years) protection from backshore erosion by absorbing wave energy along the dune face. Their application is restricted to the upper part of sandy beaches, since they are not sufficiently durable to withstand regular direct wave action. They should not be installed on shingle beaches because wear and tear will rapidly cause damage to the baskets. As they are porous structures they will tend to trap wind blown sand and allow the growth of vegetation under favourable conditions. This only applies to sloping structures: steep walls of cubic baskets will not attract sand or allow dune vegetation regrowth.

Gabions provide a short term alternative to rock armour structures in areas where large rocks are not available at an acceptable cost, or where long term protection is not appropriate.

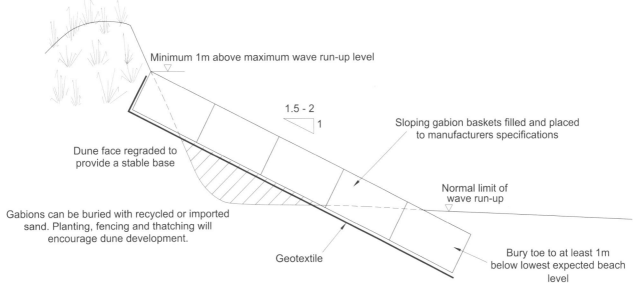

Minimum 1m above maximum wave run-up level

1.5 - 2
1

Sloping gabion baskets filled and placed to manufacturers specifications

Dune face regraded to provide a stable base

Normal limit of wave run-up

Gabions can be buried with recycled or imported sand. Planting, fencing and thatching will encourage dune development.

Geotextile

Bury toe to at least 1m below lowest expected beach level

Cross section of gabion revetment

Methods

Small gabion structures can be designed and built by volunteer groups, but larger schemes should make use of a competent coastal consultant and contractors.

The manufacturers recommendations should be followed as regards basket materials, methods of filling, lacing up of individual panels and the placement of spacer wires needed to maintain panel shape. The need for careful hand packing cannot be over emphasised. Poorly packed gabions will be rapidly damaged due to abrasion caused by movement of the stone.

Gabions used in lower energy or estuary situations can use PVC coated wire. Under more active conditions the coating is soon cracked, becoming relatively useless in preventing corrosion. In general galvanised wire of a larger diameter will provide better service than finer non-galvanised wire with a PVC coating.

The use of angular stone is not recommended as once the cages are broken the stones will be dispersed rapidly creating an unnatural beach. Mobile rocks on the beach may accelerate damage to adjacent gabion baskets.

Damaged gabions forming a public safety hazard and releasing non-indigenous cobbles onto the beach.

Gabions should be placed as a sloping revetment as shown in the figures. Near vertical gabion walls are more likely to suffer toe scour and structural collapse as they are less able to dissipate wave energy during storm wave attack. They are also much more obtrusive to the dune landscape and will not become buried by new foredunes.

The figure provides some guidance for structure design, but this should be reviewed for each site. Structure face slopes are a compromise between flatter faces that absorb more wave energy, and therefore suffer less toe scour, and steeper faces that give the structure a smaller footprint. A slope of 1:2 is a reasonable compromise, and is in keeping with natural dune slopes.

The approximate limits of wave run-up can be established by observing and recording the location of the strand line over Spring tide periods during both winter storms and more normal wave conditions. The toe of a freshly eroded dune face is normally just below the run-up limit of the most recent severe sea.

During placement, regrading of the beach/dunes may have to be carried out so as to adequately bed the baskets. A suitable geotextile should be used to prevent the underlying sand from being washed out through the gabions. Manufacturer recommendations should be followed as regards appropriate materials and installation methods. Edge details should be carefully addressed to prevent exposure of unsightly lengths of textile. Landward edges can be buried to fix the geotextile during gabion placement and filling. Seaward edges should be trimmed or firmly secured.

Small schemes can be undertaken by hand, apart form the transport and delivery of rock. Larger schemes will need heavy equipment to regrade the dune face, excavate trenches for the foundation layer of baskets and transport rock from stock piles to the baskets. Even on large schemes baskets must be hand packed to ensure minimum post-fill movement and settlement.

Burial with recycled sand, combined with vegetation transplanting, thatching and/or fencing (Summaries 2 to 5) can enhance the recovery of the dunes over the gabions. Buried revetments provide a final line of storm protection, while allowing a natural dune/beach system to develop under less extreme conditions.

As with all engineered shoreline structures, gabion revetments are likely to suffer from local scour and possible outflanking at the junction between structure and adjacent unprotected dune face. This problem can be minimised by turning the revetment face back into the dunes and burying the end into the dune face. This feathered end may extend alongshore over 20m-40m and may end 5m-10m landward of the main structure face. These dimensions will depend on the expected rate of short and long term erosion. If erosion is likely to average more than about 1m per year then gabions may well be inappropriate for defence.

Regular basket maintenance is required to maximise the life of gabions. Severely damaged baskets should be refilled and closed with new mesh panels. Replacement mesh should be laid over the entire structure if abrasion or corrosion is widespread. Under exposed conditions a maximum life of 10 years should be anticipated, after which time a replacement structure may be required.

Schemes are best implemented in the spring and early summer when work windows are least restricted and the shoreline has the greatest chance to stabilise before winter storms start to erode the upper beach.

Costs for gabion schemes depend on required dimensions, labour, availability of fill material, transport methods and the amount of minor works required to enhance the dune system. Small schemes using volunteer labour and locally available fill material may cost as little as £5,000/100m frontage. Large gabion revetments built by contractors may have an initial cost of £500,000/km, plus minor ongoing management works such as recycling to bury the gabions or other works to enhance the dune system. Economic analysis should anticipate no more than a 10 year life expectancy.

Impacts

Gabions become unsightly and dangerous if they are damaged and not properly repaired. Released cobbles are not a problem to coastal processes, but can detract from the general dune/beach environment and may accelerate damage to adjacent baskets.

Exposed gabions tend to trap strand line debris. As with all fixed dune defences the gabions will interfere with the natural dynamic interchange of material between beach and dune. They will also influence the longshore transfer of sand, modify dune habitats, disrupt the natural landform and potentially result in localised dune face scour at their terminal ends.

Vertical gabion walls are more prone to structural failure and outflanking, more intrusive on the landscape and are much less likely to become buried by new foredunes relative to sloping gabion revetments.

Best practice and environmental opportunities

Sloping gabions can provide good erosion protection for periods up to 10 years (longer if normally buried). They are often more acceptable and less costly than rock armour. When carefully built and placed they can blend into the dune landscape, and are only exposed during eroding storms. They are best used in areas where episodic erosion takes place and where natural burial by new foredunes is possible under favourable conditions. Their applicability in areas subject to persistent erosion is limited to temporary protection. Removal of temporary structures is more difficult with gabions than with sand bag, rock or timber structures. Recycling, fencing and transplanting will encourage growth of new foredunes over buried structures.

Gabion revetments may permit sand accumulation and dune grass growth.

Embryo dune formation upon a sloping gabion revetment (hidden). The dune slope above the gabion wall has been reprofiled and replanted with marram grass.

All dune management schemes should observe the following guidelines to maximise the probability of success and minimise impacts on the natural and human environment:

- Each dune erosion site must be considered independently, with management approaches tailored to the specific site.
- A policy of "Adaptive management" (Summary 1) should be considered for all sites before other options are assessed.
- Work should not be undertaken unless the beach-dune system and nearshore coastal processes have been monitored over several years and a reasonable understanding of the physical and natural environment has been established. Hasty responses to erosion may prove to be either unnecessary or damaging.
- No work of a permanent nature should be undertaken unless important immovable or irreplaceable backshore assets are at risk.

- Local interest groups, such as landowners, nature trusts, fishing associations and recreational users, should be consulted early to ensure that a broad view of the shoreline and nearshore zone is considered prior to implementing any particular management approach.
- Consideration must always be given to both long term "average" and short term extreme weather and sea conditions to determine the life expectancy of any operations.
- Consideration must be given to the consequences of failure, such as construction debris spread along the beach, public safety hazards, loss of amenity access, deterioration of the landscape, etc.
- Work should be planned and scheduled to limit damage to fragile ecosystems and to recreation. Consideration should be given to vegetation, bird nesting and migration, intertidal invertebrates, fisheries, public access, noise levels and public safety.
- All site staff must be made aware of the need for careful working practises to avoid environmental damage, and to avoid hazards associated with steep and unstable dune faces.
- Temporary or permanent management access routes to the dune face for materials, equipment and labour must be planned and constructed to minimise trampling damage to the dunes and to limit the formation of blowouts. Boardwalks or other temporary surfaces should be laid and should follow the natural contours of the dunes rather than cutting straight lines susceptible to wind erosion. Fencing should be used to stabilise sand adjacent to the track.
- Public access routes to the beach should be clearly laid out and fenced where necessary to prevent trampling that may lead to blowouts.
- Educational displays at backshore car parking areas or along footpaths should be used to explain management schemes and encourage public interest and support for the management objectives.
- Warning signs should be set up highlighting the dangers of unstable dune faces, any construction work in progress or any other hazards associated with the management schemes (gaps in rock structures, slippery algal growth, buried defences, submerged structures, mud deposits, etc)
- Post project monitoring should be undertaken at least bi-annually to assess the beach-dune evolution and the success of the scheme relative to the objectives. Appendix 2 of this guide provides monitoring guidelines.

In addition to these general guidelines, the following are of specific importance to gabion revetments:

- Sloping gabion revetments are almost always preferable to near vertical structures. They are hydraulically more efficient, more likely to be buried by sand and re-vegetated to form new foredunes. They are less intrusive on the landscape and provide less of a public safety hazard when used as a beach access route.
- Safe public access routes should be provided across the gabions, using timber or concrete steps connected to controlled paths through the dune system. This will reduce damage to baskets.
- The beach-structure interface should be kept as high up the foreshore as possible, preferably above the normal wave run up limit so that the gabions are only influential during storms. If necessary the existing dune face should be cut back and regraded to ensure that waves do not normally reach the gabions.
- Where possible recycling, fencing and transplanting should be undertaken to establish a new line of foredunes over the gabions. Burial will increase gabion life, while the new dunes will enhance the coastal landscape, provide additional erosion protection and re-establish a natural succession of dune habitats from the shoreline to the backshore.
- Near vertical structures are to be avoided, but may afford very short term headland protection to a valuable backshore asset while alternative management options are planned and implemented. They have the advantage of limiting the structure footprint.
- Inspections should be repeated at least bi-annually, preferably at times when beach levels are low. Maintenance work should be completed as soon as damage is observed.

Summary 9: ARTIFICIAL HEADLANDS

APPROPRIATE LOCATIONS	Rapidly eroding dunes with important backshore assets at discrete intervals along the shore.
COSTS	Moderate, but low maintenance (£20,000-£60,000/100m of structure, plus minor works for unprotected frontages).
EFFECTIVENESS	Good temporary or long term protection for protected length. Allows natural processes to continue elsewhere. Can be used with other low cost methods. Unlimited structure life for rock headlands.
BENEFITS	Provides local protection with minimum disturbance to dune system as a whole. Can be modified or removed at later date.
PROBLEMS	Visually intrusive. Do not control erosion along the whole frontage. Structures may interfere with longshore transport, particularly on sand-gravel beaches, and may require periodic extension or relocation landward to avoid outflanking.

General description

Artificial headlands are rock structures built along the toe of eroding dunes to protect strategic points, allowing natural processes to continue along the remaining frontage. This is significantly cheaper than protecting a whole frontage and can provide temporary or long term protection to specific assets at risk. Temporary headlands can be formed of gabions or sand bags, but life expectancy will normally be between 1 and 5 years.

Rock headland protecting a golf course tee.

Function

Artificial headlands stabilise discrete lengths of the dune face while allowing the intervening stretches to erode naturally, forming an increasingly embayed shoreline. As the shoreline becomes more indented so the wave energy will be dissipated over a longer frontage and ultimately a more stable plan shape can develop. Stability will depend on the length and spacing of the headlands. Short structures with long gaps will provide local protection but may not allow a stable planshape to develop. If ongoing erosion is severe the headlands may need to be extended or relocated to prevent outflanking or structural failure, although they will continue to provide some protection as nearshore breakwaters (Summary 11).

The embayments between headlands will not become independent units as sand will be transported by wind, waves and currents along the lower foreshore to seaward of the structures. If gravel is present the headlands may restrict longshore movement along the upper beach; this can be useful to control losses if renourishment or recycling is undertaken.

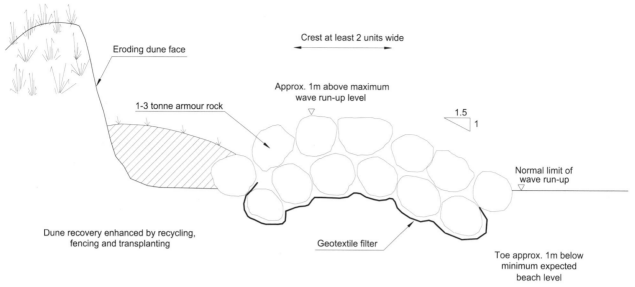

Cross-section of rock headland protecting an eroding dune face

Planview of rock headland

Methods

Small rock headland schemes can be implemented without specialist assistance, but normally the services of a competent coastal consultant and contractors are required. Information on the design of rock structures is available from the CIRIA/CUR "Manual on the use of rock in coastal and shoreline engineering". The accompanying figures provide initial guidance but this should be confirmed for each site. Temporary structures can also be formed using sand bags (Summary 6) or gabions (Summary 8), although gabions can be more difficult to remove or relocate than rock.

As with all rock structures on the shoreline the rock size, face slopes, crest elevation and crest width must be designed with care. Rock size is dependent on incident wave height, period and direction, structure slope, acceptance of risk, cross-sectional design, and the availability/cost of armour rock from quarries. In general 1-3 tonne rock will suffice, provided that it is placed as at least a double layer, with a 1:1.5 to 1:2.5 face slope, and there is an acceptance of some risk of failure. Rock size may need to increase if the toe is within the zone of regular wave action.

Randomly dumped rock with a high void to solid ratio is hydraulically more efficient than placed and packed rock. However, rock structures on recreational beaches should be built with a view to minimising the potential for accidents involving beach users slipping between rocks.

The structure should be constructed within a shallow trench and a geotextile filter should be laid under the rocks to prevent the migration of sand upwards and the settlement of the rocks into the beach. The geotextile should be wrapped around the base layer of rocks, and the rock toe should be set below the lowest expected beach level.

Concrete armour units of various types can be used instead of rock, but are normally considerably more expensive and may be considered much more visually obtrusive. The potentially greater hydraulic efficiency offered by some types of concrete units is of little importance to a dune defence structure.

Headlands should be built just seaward of the dune toe, rather than as a revetment. Increasing the distance down the beach will allow the protected dunes to retain some of their natural dynamics and appearance, and will create a more embayed shoreline, with wave energy being dissipated over a longer frontage. However if the distance is too great the structure may be outflanked, effectively forming a detached breakwater and allowing the protected dune face to be subject to erosion once more.

The approximate limits of wave run-up can be established by observing and recording the location of the strand line over Spring tide periods during both winter storms and more normal wave conditions. The toe of a freshly eroded dune face is normally just below the run-up limit of the most recent severe sea.

The length of the structure must be sufficient to protect the backshore assets at risk while adjacent dunes continue to be eroded. The structure ends must return to the eroding face, and may need extending from time to time to prevent outflanking. These end extensions can often be lower than the main structure face as they will be subject to less wave attack. By keeping the crests low there will be a greater opportunity for wind blown sand to reach the dune face.

Structures can be built to protect a single location, such as an outfall or important building, or as part of a series of headlands intended to create an embayed shoreline. Single structures may well need regular extensions to prevent outflanking if erosion of adjacent beaches is severe. Closely spaced headlands can be designed and managed to develop a stable, embayed shoreline, but each site must be considered separately by specialist consultants if a successful scheme is to be developed.

The area behind the structure can be vegetated, thatched, fenced or replenished with recycled sand (Summaries 2, 3, 4 and 5) to stabilise the dunes, and possibly encourage regeneration. This is only possible if the structure is built forward of the dune toe. If the structure is built against the dune face as a short length of revetment, the dunes will be less likely to grow forward and more erosion will occur before the adjacent shorelines begin to stabilise to a new plan shape.

Construction costs are mainly dependent on structure dimensions, but can be heavily influenced by the availability of suitable rock (or other material), transport and the associated costs of recycling or nourishment. Rock structures can be assumed to have an unlimited life with respect to economic assessments, although the benefits may be only short to medium term.

Impacts

Even though this form of defence is intended to give only partial protection to the dunes the impacts on shoreline processes and landscape will still be high, and may be unacceptable in environmentally sensitive areas. Erosion may well continue along the unprotected frontages, and, without ongoing management, the structures may be outflanked allowing erosion of the protected frontage as well.

On frontages affected by longshore transport the headlands may reduce drift rates, resulting in the erosion of downdrift stretches of coast, but helping to stabilise the updrift shore. As with all fixed dune defences, the headlands will interfere with the natural dynamic interchange of material between beach and dune. They will also influence the longshore transfer of sand, modify dune habitats, disrupt the natural landform and potentially result in localised dune face scour at their terminal ends.

Gabions forming an artificial headland and protecting outfall headworks. The gabions have been extended landward to prevent outflanking.

Best practice and environmental opportunities

Headlands can provide good protection to discrete points along the shoreline, either temporarily or over longer periods. They can also be used to transform a length of eroding dunes into a shoreline of small bays and headlands, in which part of the dune system is maintained as a dynamic system, while other lengths are artificially fixed. The width of the upper beach in the centre of the embayments may increase, providing improved recreation. The dune faces in the lee of the headlands may redevelop as blown sand can pass around the structures.

Temporary structures can be removed when no longer required, with little lasting damage to the dune system as a whole. Sandbags structures are the easiest to remove, but rock structures can also be taken away for re-use elsewhere.

All dune management schemes should observe the following guidelines to maximise the probability of success and minimise impacts on the natural and human environment:

- Each dune erosion site must be considered independently, with management approaches tailored to the specific site.
- A policy of "Adaptive management" (Summary 1) should be considered for all sites before other options are assessed.
- Work should not be undertaken unless the beach-dune system and nearshore coastal processes have been monitored over several years and a reasonable understanding of the physical and natural environment has been established. Hasty responses to erosion may prove to be either unnecessary or damaging.
- No work of a permanent nature should be undertaken unless important immovable or irreplaceable backshore assets are at risk.
- Local interest groups, such as landowners, nature trusts, fishing associations and recreational users, should be consulted early to ensure that a broad view of the shoreline and nearshore zone is considered prior to implementing any particular management approach.
- Consideration must always be given to both long term "average" and short term extreme weather and sea conditions to determine the life expectancy of any operations.
- Consideration must be given to the consequences of failure, such as construction debris spread along the beach, public safety hazards, loss of amenity access, deterioration of the landscape, etc.
- Work should be planned and scheduled to limit damage to fragile ecosystems and to recreation. Consideration should be given to vegetation, bird nesting and migration, intertidal invertebrates, fisheries, public access, noise levels and public safety.
- All site staff must be made aware of the need for careful working practises to avoid environmental damage, and to avoid hazards associated with steep and unstable dune faces.
- Temporary or permanent management access routes to the dune face for materials, equipment and labour must be planned and constructed to minimise trampling damage to the dunes and to limit the formation of blowouts. Boardwalks or other temporary surfaces should be laid and should follow the natural contours of the dunes rather than cutting straight lines susceptible to wind erosion. Fencing should be used to stabilise sand adjacent to the track.
- Public access routes to the beach should be clearly laid out and fenced where necessary to prevent trampling that may lead to blowouts.
- Educational displays at backshore car parking areas or along footpaths should be used to explain management schemes and encourage public interest and support for the management objectives.
- Warning signs should be set up highlighting the dangers of unstable dune faces, any construction work in progress or any other hazards associated with the management schemes (gaps in rock structures, slippery algal growth, buried defences, submerged structures, mud deposits, etc)
- Post project monitoring should be undertaken at least bi-annually to assess the beach-dune evolution and the success of the scheme relative to the objectives. Appendix 2 of this guide provides monitoring guidelines.

In addition to these general guidelines, the following are of specific importance to artificial headlands:

- Further guidance on the design of rock structures is available from the CIRIA/CUR "Manual on the use of rock in coastal and shoreline engineering".

- Where possible recycling, fencing and transplanting should be undertaken to establish a new line of foredunes behind the headlands and along the unprotected upper beach. These dunes will enhance the coastal landscape, provide additional erosion protection and re-establish a natural succession of dune habitats from the shoreline to the backshore.

- Headland ends should be extended alongshore and landwards to avoid outflanking if the adjacent dunes erode rapidly. Other structure dimensions, such as crest elevation, can also be modified if monitoring indicates that the initial layout is not achieving the required objectives. Any observed storm damage, such as displaced rocks, should be rectified during maintenance operations.

- The use of local rock should not be a requirement of design unless there are genuine landscape considerations, such as adjacent rocky outcrops; even in this instance local rock should only be used if it is readily available in the size range required and is a sound material for coastal construction.

- The use of builder's rubble is unlikely to ever be appropriate for dune management. Most material is too small to be effective and will be drawn down the beach during any significant storm. The rubble may contain material that is either hazardous to beach users, toxic or simply unattractive. Large concrete slabs may be acceptable from an engineering perspective but are unlikely to meet approval with respect to their landscape impact or their safety for use in a public area.

Summary 10: ARTIFICIAL REEFS

APPROPRIATE LOCATIONS	Exposed dunes of high ecological and landscape value.
COSTS	Moderate to high, and may need some shoreline maintenance (£20,000 to £60,000/100m of structure, plus minor works for unprotected areas).
EFFECTIVENESS	Causes lee side accretion, but least effective during storm surge conditions. Unlimited structure life.
BENEFITS	Natural processes are only partly disrupted, allowing dunes to stabilise. Rocks create new intertidal habitat.
PROBLEMS	May cause navigation hazard. Visually intrusive at low tide. Disrupt amenity use of beach.

General description

Artificial reefs are shore parallel rock mound structures set part way down the beach face. They may be long single structures or form a series of reefs extending for some distance alongshore. They are distinguished from Nearshore Breakwaters (Summary 11) by being submerged for at least part of the tidal cycle, and are therefore less intrusive on the coastal landscape, have less impact on upper beach longshore processes and add a new intertidal habitat to sandy foreshores.

Function

Reefs dissipate part of the incident wave energy before it reaches the dune face, protecting the upper beach from erosion and encouraging deposition. Long structures (sills) reduce wave energy over an extended frontage, resulting in a more stable upper beach and dune face. Shorter, segmented reefs protect short lengths of the shore, allowing erosion to continue elsewhere. The result is an embayed shoreline with upper beach deposits (salients) forming behind the reefs.

Salients will allow new foredunes to develop, but this accretion may be at the expense of continued erosion elsewhere. Recycling or nourishment, followed by fencing, thatching and transplanting may address this problem, and will enhance the rate of dune-beach recovery. Reefs have less impact on upper beach transport processes than nearshore breakwaters, and can be used on open beaches. In particular, tombolos will not form behind low level reefs, but can form with higher breakwaters; tombolos would significantly disrupt longshore drift, potentially causing downdrift erosion.

Reefs are of little use within estuaries where currents, rather than waves, are the main erosive force.

Methods

Small reef schemes can be implemented without specialist assistance, but normally the services of a competent coastal consultant and contractors are required. Information on the design of rock structures is available from the CIRIA/CUR "Manual on the use of rock in coastal and shoreline engineering". The accompanying figures provide initial guidance but this should be confirmed for each site.

As with all rock structures on the shoreline the rock size, face slopes, crest elevation and crest width must be designed with care. Rock size is dependent on incident wave height, period and direction, structure slope, acceptance of risk, cross-sectional design, and the availability/cost of armour rock from quarries. In general 3-6 tonne rock will suffice, provided that it is placed as at least a double layer, with a 1:1.5 to 1:2.5 face slope, and there is an acceptance of some risk of failure. This assumes a structure location close to the mid-tide level of the beach. Rock size or side slopes may need to increase if the reefs are built further down the beach face where wave action is stronger.

Randomly dumped rock with a high void to solid ratio is hydraulically more efficient than placed and packed rock. However, rock structures on recreational beaches should be built with a view to minimising the potential for accidents involving beach users slipping between rocks.

The structures should be constructed within a shallow trench and a geotextile filter should be laid under the rocks to prevent the migration of sand upwards and the settlement of the rocks into the beach. The geotextile should be wrapped around the base layer of rocks, and the rock toe should be set below the lowest expected beach level.

The crest elevation will have a major impact on the extent of wave energy dissipation. Some erosion protection will be achieved if the crest is as much as 2m below the water level during storms. Energy dissipation will increase as the crest rises up, until the point at which the structure is rarely submerged. An elevation close to the

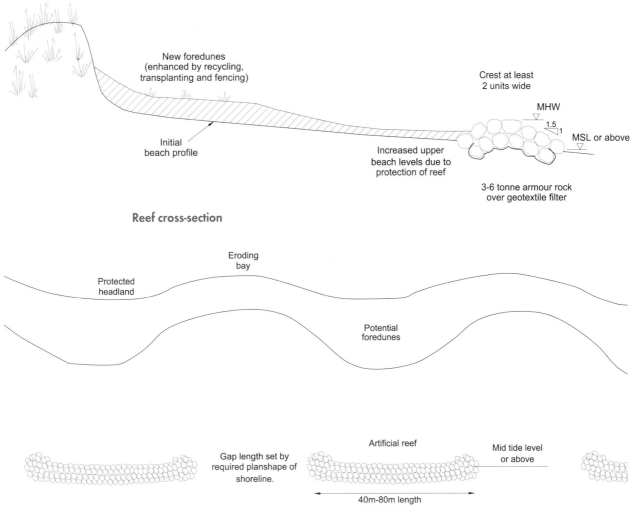

Reef cross-section

Planview of a series of reefs

Labels in figure:

New foredunes (enhanced by recycling, transplanting and fencing)

Crest at least 2 units wide

MHW

1.5
1

MSL or above

Initial beach profile

Increased upper beach levels due to protection of reef

3-6 tonne armour rock over geotextile filter

Protected headland

Eroding bay

Potential foredunes

Gap length set by required planshape of shoreline.

Artificial reef

Mid tide level or above

40m-80m length

mean high tide level should be acceptable as a first approximation. A crest much above this level effectively converts a reef to a detached breakwater, introducing the potential for the formation of harmful tombolos and disruption to longshore processes.

Wave energy dissipation will increase with crest width, but significant dissipation is not achieved until the width equals about half of the wave period (say 30m – 50m). Widths of this magnitude are simply not practical, so structure crests are usually restricted to 2-3 rock diameters.

Reefs may actually increase shoreline problems if they are used in areas subject to strong nearshore tidal currents. Scour along the seaward face and around the ends of reefs should be monitored, and structure maintenance undertaken prior to failure where beach levels drop.

The ends of each reef should be formed into a roundhead with shallower side slopes, particularly along the landward face. The roundhead reduces the tendency for local scour and improves the stability of the structure.

Concrete armour units of various types can be used instead of rock, but are normally considerably more expensive. The potentially greater hydraulic efficiency of some units is of no importance to dune defence structures and the units are normally considered to be more unattractive than rock armour.

There is little guidance available for the length and spacing of reefs. Numerical modelling should be undertaken by a competent coastal consultant during preliminary studies. Longer or higher structures will provide greater protection but will also increase potential long shore impacts. Wider gaps will allow greater shoreline erosion, which may threaten assets. Structure dimensions can vary along the length of a scheme to provide varying levels of backshore protection.

The area behind the structures can be built up by recycling or nourishment (Summaries 5 and 7), and then grassed, thatched and fenced (Summaries 2, 3, and 4) to stabilise the dunes and possibly encourage regeneration.

Costs for reef schemes depend on structure dimensions and spacings. They can be heavily influenced by the availability of suitable rock (or other material), transport and the costs of any recycling or nourishment. Work windows are limited to low tide periods and may be influenced by stormy seas. Rock structures can be assumed to have an unlimited life with respect to economic assessments.

Impacts

Even though this form of defence is intended to give only partial protection to the shoreline the impacts on shoreline processes, intertidal habitats and landscape will still be high, and may be unacceptable in environmentally sensitive areas. Erosion in the lee of the gaps may well continue for several years after construction while a new beach planshape develops. Long, sill type, reefs with no gaps may suffer from a build up of fine sediment, seaweed or other debris along the inshore side - gaps provide a flushing mechanism.

As the structures are separated from the shore as the tide rises, and then become submerged, they are potentially hazardous to anyone using them as a perch. Rocks below the level of Spring tides will tend to be covered with marine growth including slippery algae, again forming a public hazard.

The submerged reefs will form a hazard for water sports and navigation, and must be clearly marked with appropriate beacons. Wave induced currents around the ends of reefs can be locally strong and a danger to swimmers.

Best practice and environmental opportunities

The width of the upper beach along the embayed shoreline may increase, providing improved recreation. New foredunes may develop in the lee of the reefs. The structures allow natural beach-dune processes to continue, albeit along a modified shoreline.

The reefs will form a new intertidal habitat, bringing rocky shore communities to a sandy beach. The structures may well prove to be popular with beach users.

All dune management schemes should observe the following guidelines to maximise the probability of success and minimise impacts on the natural and human environment:

- Each dune erosion site must be considered independently, with management approaches tailored to the specific site.
- A policy of "Adaptive management" (Summary 1) should be considered for all sites before other options are assessed.
- Work should not be undertaken unless the beach-dune system and nearshore coastal processes have been monitored over several years and a reasonable understanding of the physical and natural environment has been established. Hasty responses to erosion may prove to be either unnecessary or damaging.
- No work of a permanent nature should be undertaken unless important immovable or irreplaceable backshore assets are at risk.
- Local interest groups, such as landowners, nature trusts, fishing associations and recreational users, should be consulted early to ensure that a broad view of the shoreline and nearshore zone is considered prior to implementing any particular management approach.
- Consideration must always be given to both long term "average" and short term extreme weather and sea conditions to determine the life expectancy of any operations.
- Consideration must be given to the consequences of failure, such as construction debris spread along the beach, public safety hazards, loss of amenity access, deterioration of the landscape, etc.
- Work should be planned and scheduled to limit damage to fragile ecosystems and to recreation. Consideration should be given to vegetation, bird nesting and migration, intertidal invertebrates, fisheries, public access, noise levels and public safety.
- All site staff must be made aware of the need for careful working practises to avoid environmental damage, and to avoid hazards associated with steep and unstable dune faces.
- Temporary or permanent management access routes to the dune face for materials, equipment and labour must be planned and constructed to minimise trampling damage to the dunes and to limit the formation of blowouts. Boardwalks or other temporary surfaces should be laid and should follow the natural contours of the dunes rather than cutting straight lines susceptible to wind erosion. Fencing should be used to stabilise sand adjacent to the track.
- Public access routes to the beach should be clearly laid out and fenced where necessary to prevent trampling that may lead to blowouts.

- Educational displays at backshore car parking areas or along footpaths should be used to explain management schemes and encourage public interest and support for the management objectives.
- Warning signs should be set up highlighting the dangers of unstable dune faces, any construction work in progress or any other hazards associated with the management schemes (gaps in rock structures, slippery algal growth, buried defences, submerged structures, mud deposits, etc)
- Post project monitoring should be undertaken at least bi-annually to assess the beach-dune evolution and the success of the scheme relative to the objectives. Appendix 2 of this guide provides monitoring guidelines.

In addition to these general guidelines, the following are of specific importance to artificial reefs:

- Further guidance on the design of rock structures is available from the CIRIA/CUR "Manual on the use of rock in coastal and shoreline engineering" and from the CIRIA "Beach management manual".
- Reef construction may need to be accompanied by an ongoing programme of beach recycling or nourishment to ensure that sediment redistribution is not unduly damaging to unprotected frontages. Regular monitoring and management are required to establish a successful scheme. Monitoring must include adjacent shorelines as well as those immediately within the reef scheme.
- Monitoring should also record any scour around the structures that may indicate potential for structural failure or the presence of strong local currents that may be a hazard to beach users.
- Structures should be kept to a minimum size to reduce visual impact. Structure dimensions can be modified if monitoring indicates that the initial layout is not achieving the required objectives. Any observed storm damage, such as displaced rocks, should be rectified during maintenance operations.
- Where possible recycling, fencing and transplanting should be undertaken to establish a new line of foredunes in the lee of the reefs. These dunes will improve the coastal landscape, provide additional erosion protection and re-establish a natural succession of dune habitats from the shoreline to the backshore.
- As reefs are submerged over part of the tidal cycle they will need to be marked by navigation beacons and their positions recorded with the Hydrographic Office.
- The use of local rock should not be a requirement of design unless there are genuine landscape considerations, such as adjacent rocky outcrops; even in this instance local rock should only be used if it is readily available in the size range required and is a sound material for coastal construction.
- The use of builder's rubble is unlikely to ever be appropriate for dune management. Most material is too small to be effective and will be drawn down the beach during any significant storm. The rubble may contain material that is either hazardous to beach users, toxic or simply unattractive. Large concrete slabs may be acceptable from an engineering perspective but are unlikely to meet approval with respect to their landscape impact or their safety for use in a public area.

Summary 11: NEARSHORE BREAKWATERS

APPROPRIATE LOCATIONS	High value frontages with low rates of longshore transport, and weak nearshore tidal currents.
COSTS	High, but low maintenance (£40,000-£100,000/100m of structure, plus minor works for unprotected)
EFFECTIVENESS	Cause lee side accretion and erosion behind gaps. Offers good protection within enclosed bays, but potentially damaging to open coasts.
BENEFITS	Dunes not directly disturbed, increases area of dry upper beach, may allow new foredunes to stabilise. Unlimited structure life.
PROBLEMS	Visually intrusive, alter upper beach morphology, may cause fine sediment, seaweed or debris to accumulate along upper beach. Can cause locally strong currents and may be a hazard to beach users.

General description

Nearshore breakwaters are segmented, shore parallel structures built along the upper beach at approximately high water mark. They are normally built of rock, but can be formed of concrete armour units. At maximum tide levels their crests are still visible, but they may be separated from the shoreline. The gaps allow some wave energy to reach the upper beach and even the dune face.

These structures are distinguished from Artificial Reefs (Summary 10) that are built further down the foreshore and are submerged at high tide.

Nearshore breakwaters on the upper foreshore in the Dornoch Firth, shortly after construction.

The same breakwaters as illustrated above, seven years after construction. Note relative stability of backshore.

88

Function

Breakwaters reduce the energy of waves reaching the shoreline, but do not completely isolate dunes from the natural beach processes. The structures act as a direct barrier to waves, but at very high water levels they allow some overtopping. The gaps between segmented structures allow some wave energy to reach the upper beach and dune face, but this is dissipated by refraction and diffraction. Erosion may continue in the lee of the gaps leading to formation of an embayed shoreline as sand moves into the shelter of the structures.

Sand build up in the lee of the structures (salients) may grow seawards sufficiently to connect with the structure, forming a "tombolo". If the salient is stable, new foredunes may develop. Recycling or nourishment followed by fencing, thatching and transplanting may be used to accelerate formation of stable salients and dunes.

Breakwaters can have a strong influence on longshore drift and should not normally be used on long expanses of open coast or within estuaries if strong wave or tidally induced currents are present. Breakwaters can cause downdrift erosion or result in dangerous conditions for beach users.

Nearshore breakwaters are distinct from the much larger "detached", "offshore" or "island" breakwaters that are also not submerged at high tide but are built further down the foreshore or even beyond the low water mark. These alternative forms are generally regarded as inappropriate for most UK coastal situations as they are extremely intrusive on the landscape, expensive to build and are very difficult to design with any degree of confidence regarding their long term effect on the local and adjacent shorelines.

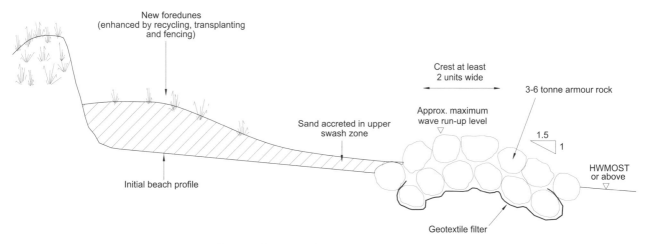

Cross section of a nearshore breakwater protecting an eroding dune face

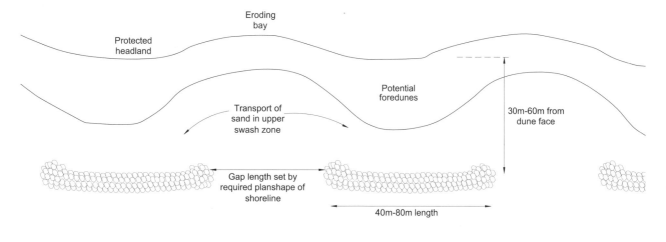

Plan view of a system of nearshore breakwaters

Methods

Breakwater schemes can have a significant impact on the shoreline and should not be implemented without specialist assistance from a competent coastal consultant and contractors. Information on the design of rock structures is available from the CIRIA/CUR "Manual on the use of rock in coastal and shoreline engineering". The accompanying figures provide initial guidance but this should be confirmed for each site.

As with all rock structures on the shoreline the rock size, face slopes, crest elevation and crest width must be designed with care. Rock size is dependent on incident wave height, period and direction, structure slope, acceptance of risk, cross-sectional design, and the availability/cost of armour rock from quarries. In general 3-6 tonne rock will suffice, provided that it is placed as at least a double layer, with a 1:1.5 to 1:2.5 face slope, and there is an acceptance of some risk of failure. Rock size may need to increase if the structures are built further down the beach face where wave action is stronger.

Randomly dumped rock with a high void to solid ratio is hydraulically more efficient than placed and packed rock. However, rock structures on recreational beaches should be built with a view to minimising the potential for accidents involving beach users slipping between rocks.

The structures should be constructed within a shallow trench and a geotextile filter should be laid under the rocks to prevent the migration of sand upwards and the settlement of the rocks into the beach. The geotextile should be wrapped around the base layer of rocks, and the rock toe should be set below the lowest expected beach level.

The ends of each breakwater should be formed into a roundhead with shallower side slopes, particularly along the landward face. The roundhead reduces the tendency for local scour and improves the stability of the structure and the units are normally considered to be more unattractive than rock armour.

Concrete armour units of various types can be used instead of rock, but are normally considerably more expensive. The potentially greater hydraulic efficiency of the units is of no importance to a dune defence structure and the units are normally considered to be more unattractive than rock armour.

There is little guidance available for the length, gap widths, crest heights or distance offshore. Numerical modelling by competent coastal consultants should be undertaken during preliminary studies. As a rough guide gaps should be about half of the structure length and the length should be about equal to the distance from the initial shoreline. As the gaps widen there will be more movement of sand from the bays to the salients. Provided that no backshore assets are at risk this process can continue until tombolos form in the area protected by the breakwaters. Structure and gap lengths can vary along the scheme to provide varying levels of backshore protection. Structures should be constructed on the upper foreshore so that they can be of modest height, yet be effective in protecting the dune toe. The seaward toe should be at or above HWMOST and the crest about the level of maximum wave run-up.

The approximate limits of wave run-up can be established by observing and recording the location of the strand line over Spring tide periods during both winter storms and more normal wave conditions. The toe of a freshly eroded dune face is normally just below the run-up limit of the most recent severe sea.

The structures should be relatively modest in size, encompassing a small part of the foreshore, so as to have only a small impact on the rate of littoral drift. Breakwaters should not be used in areas where there is a moderate to strong littoral drift since they could cause downdrift erosion by cutting of the supply of material in that direction.

If there is not a large natural supply of sediments it may be necessary to recycle or import beach nourishment material (Summaries 5 and 7) to create salients in the lee of the breakwaters. Once beach material has built up above the highest tide levels, the foot of the dunes should be safe from wave action. If there is a significant build up of sand, fencing and transplanting can be used to encourage dune growth (Summaries 2 to 4).

Costs for nearshore breakwater schemes depend on structure dimensions and spacings. They can be heavily influenced by the availability of suitable rock (or other material), transport and the costs of any recycling or nourishment. Rock structures can be assumed to have an unlimited life with respect to economic assessments.

Impacts

Even though this form of defence is intended to give only partial protection to the shoreline the impacts on shoreline processes, intertidal habitats and landscape will still be high, and may be unacceptable in environmentally sensitive areas. Erosion in the lee of the gaps may well continue for several years after construction while a new beach planshape develops.

On frontages affected by longshore transport the breakwaters may reduce drift rates, resulting in the erosion of downdrift stretches of coast, but helping to stabilise the updrift shore.

As the structures may be separated from the shore at peak water levels they are potentially hazardous to anyone using them as a perch and becoming stranded as the tide rises, particularly if there are also heavy seas.

Where the nearshore waters tend to be silty the breakwaters may encourage lee-side deposition of mud leading to both unwanted odours and unsafe beach areas. Other lee side deposits may include sea weed and jetsam from ships (plastic containers, nets, rope, etc)

Wave induced currents around the ends of breakwaters can be locally strong and a danger to beach users.

Best practice and environmental opportunities

The width of the upper beach along the embayed shoreline may increase, providing improved recreation. New foredunes may develop in the lee of the breakwaters. The structures allow natural beach-dune processes to continue, albeit along a modified shoreline. Existing dune habitats and land forms may be retained and/or enhanced in the areas behind the structures.

All dune management schemes should observe the following guidelines to maximise the probability of success and minimise impacts on the natural and human environment:

- Each dune erosion site must be considered independently, with management approaches tailored to the specific site.
- A policy of "Adaptive management" (Summary 1) should be considered for all sites before other options are assessed.
- Work should not be undertaken unless the beach-dune system and nearshore coastal processes have been monitored over several years and a reasonable understanding of the physical and natural environment has been established. Hasty responses to erosion may prove to be either unnecessary or damaging.
- No work of a permanent nature should be undertaken unless important immovable or irreplaceable backshore assets are at risk.
- Local interest groups, such as landowners, nature trusts, fishing associations and recreational users, should be consulted early to ensure that a broad view of the shoreline and nearshore zone is considered prior to implementing any particular management approach.
- Consideration must always be given to both long term "average" and short term extreme weather and sea conditions to determine the life expectancy of any operations.
- Consideration must be given to the consequences of failure, such as construction debris spread along the beach, public safety hazards, loss of amenity access, deterioration of the landscape, etc.
- Work should be planned and scheduled to limit damage to fragile ecosystems and to recreation. Consideration should be given to vegetation, bird nesting and migration, intertidal invertebrates, fisheries, public access, noise levels and public safety.
- All site staff must be made aware of the need for careful working practises to avoid environmental damage, and to avoid hazards associated with steep and unstable dune faces.
- Temporary or permanent management access routes to the dune face for materials, equipment and labour must be planned and constructed to minimise trampling damage to the dunes and to limit the formation of blowouts. Boardwalks or other temporary surfaces should be laid and should follow the natural contours of the dunes rather than cutting straight lines susceptible to wind erosion. Fencing should be used to stabilise sand adjacent to the track.
- Public access routes to the beach should be clearly laid out and fenced where necessary to prevent trampling that may lead to blowouts.
- Educational displays at backshore car parking areas or along footpaths should be used to explain management schemes and encourage public interest and support for the management objectives.
- Warning signs should be set up highlighting the dangers of unstable dune faces, any construction work in progress or any other hazards associated with the management schemes (gaps in rock structures, slippery algal growth, buried defences, submerged structures, mud deposits, etc)
- Post project monitoring should be undertaken at least bi-annually to assess the beach-dune evolution and the success of the scheme relative to the objectives. Appendix 2 of this guide provides monitoring guidelines.

In addition to these general guidelines, the following are of specific importance to nearshore breakwaters:

- Further guidance on the design of rock structures is available from the CIRIA/CUR "Manual on the use of rock in coastal and shoreline engineering" and from the CIRIA "Beach management manual".

- Breakwater construction may need to be accompanied by an ongoing programme of beach recycling or nourishment to ensure that sediment redistribution is not unduly damaging to unprotected frontages. Regular monitoring and management are required to establish a successful scheme. Monitoring must include adjacent shorelines as well as those immediately within the breakwater scheme.

- Monitoring should also record any scour around the structures that may indicate potential for structural failure or the presence of strong local currents that may be a hazard to beach users.

- Structures should be kept to a minimum size to reduce visual impact. Structure dimensions can be modified if monitoring indicates that the initial layout is not achieving the required objectives. Any observed storm damage, such as displaced rocks, should be rectified during maintenance operations.

- Where possible recycling, fencing and transplanting should be undertaken to establish a new line of foredunes in the lee of the breakwaters. These dunes will enhance the coastal landscape, provide additional erosion protection and re-establish a natural succession of dune habitats from the shoreline to the backshore.

- The use of local rock should not be a requirement of design unless there are genuine landscape considerations, such as adjacent rocky outcrops; even in this instance local rock should only be used if it is readily available in the size range required and is a sound material for coastal construction.

- The use of builder's rubble is unlikely to ever be appropriate for dune management. Most material is too small to be effective and will be drawn down the beach during any significant storm. The rubble may contain material that is either hazardous to beach users, toxic or simply unattractive. Large concrete slabs may be acceptable from an engineering perspective but are unlikely to meet approval with respect to their landscape impact or their safety for use in a public area.

Summary 12: GROYNES

APPROPRIATE LOCATIONS	High value frontages influenced by strong long shore processes (wave induced or tidal currents) where nourishment or recycling are undertaken. Best on shingle beaches or within estuaries.
COSTS	Moderate, but must include for recycling or nourishment (£10,000-£100,000 per structure, plus recycling).
EFFECTIVENESS	Good on exposed shorelines with a natural shingle upper beach. Can also be useful in estuaries to deflect flows. Unlimited structure life for rock groynes.
BENEFITS	Encourages upper beach stability and reduces maintenance commitment for recycling or nourishment.
PROBLEMS	Disrupts natural processes and public access along upper beach. Likely to cause downdrift erosion if beach is not managed.

General description

Groynes are cross-shore structures designed to reduce longshore transport on open beaches or to deflect nearshore currents within an estuary. On an open beach they are normally built as a series to influence a long section of shoreline that has been nourished or is managed by recycling. In an estuary they may be single structures.

Rock is often favoured as the construction material, but timber or gabions can be used for temporary structures of varying life expectancies (timber: 10-25 years, gabions: 1-5 years). Groynes are often used in combination with revetments to provide a high level of erosion protection.

Recently built rock groyne at estuary mouth, constructed in association with beach renourishment of adjacent foreshore.

Function

Groynes reduce longshore transport by trapping beach material and causing the beach orientation to change relative to the dominant wave directions. They mainly influence bedload transport and are most effective on shingle or gravel beaches. Sand is carried in temporary suspension during higher energy wave or current conditions and will therefore tend to be carried over or around any cross-shore structures. Groynes can also be used successfully in estuaries to alter nearshore tidal flow patterns.

Rock groynes have the advantages of simple construction, long-term durability and ability to absorb some wave energy due to their semi-permeable nature. Wooden groynes are less durable and tend to reflect, rather than absorb energy. Gabions can be useful as temporary groynes but have a short life expectancy.

Groynes along a duned beach must have at least a short "T" section of revetment at their landward end to prevent outflanking during storm events. The revetment will be less obtrusive if it is normally buried by the foredunes.

Beach recycling or nourishment (Summaries 5 and 7) is normally required to maximise the effectiveness of groynes. On their own, they will cause downdrift erosion as beach material is held within the groyne bays.

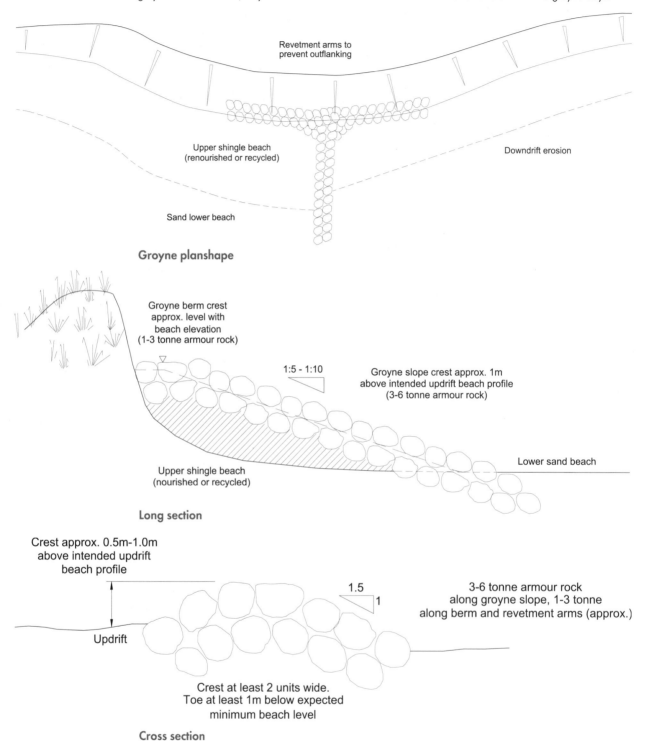

Revetment arms to
prevent outflanking

Upper shingle beach
(renourished or recycled)

Downdrift erosion

Sand lower beach

Groyne planshape

Groyne berm crest
approx. level with
beach elevation
(1-3 tonne armour rock)

1:5 - 1:10

Groyne slope crest approx. 1m
above intended updrift beach profile
(3-6 tonne armour rock)

Lower sand beach

Upper shingle beach
(nourished or recycled)

Long section

Crest approx. 0.5m-1.0m
above intended updrift
beach profile

1.5
1

3-6 tonne armour rock
along groyne slope, 1-3 tonne
along berm and revetment arms (approx.)

Updrift

Crest at least 2 units wide.
Toe at least 1m below expected
minimum beach level

Cross section

Methods

Groynes can have a significant impact on the shoreline, and schemes should always be undertaken under the supervision of a competent coastal consultant. Information on the design of rock structures is available from the CIRIA/CUR "Manual on the use of rock in coastal and shoreline engineering" with further detailed guidance on the use of groynes found in the CIRIA "Beach Management Manual". The accompanying figures provide initial guidance but this should be confirmed for each site. Temporary structures can be formed using sand bags (Summary 6) or gabions (Summary 8), although gabions can be more to remove or relocate than rock.

As with all rock structures on the shoreline the rock size, face slopes, crest elevation and crest width must be designed with care. Rock size is dependent on incident wave height, period and direction, structure slope, acceptance of risk, cross-sectional design, and the availability/cost of armour rock from quarries. In general 1-3 tonne rock will suffice for the landward parts of the groynes, provided that it is placed as at least a double layer, with a 1:1.5 to 1:2.5 face slope, and there is an acceptance of some risk of failure. Larger rock, probably 3-6 tonne, may be needed for the more exposed body and seaward head of each structure.

Randomly dumped rock with a high void to solid ratio is hydraulically more efficient than placed and packed rock. However, rock structures on recreational beaches should be built with a view to minimising the potential for accidents involving beach users slipping between rocks.

The groynes should be built prior to nourishment, with the rocks being laid into a shallow trench. On gravel beaches a geotextile is not normally required, as upward sediment migration is less important than on a sand beach. The groyne berm should be built to the anticipated crest level of the beach. The groyne berm length should equal the intended crest width of the updrift beach. The groyne should extend down the beach at a level of about 1m above the anticipated updrift shingle beach, normally at a slope of about 1:5 to 1:10. The groyne head should extend down into the sand beach, allowing for some future erosion. On a shingle beach there is not significant benefit to creating any novel head extensions

The groyne-dune interface may need additional protection to reduce the possibility of outflanking. Short lengths of revetment, longer on the downdrift side, will ensure greater resistance to storm erosion. Where a high degree of erosion protection is required it may be necessary to construct a full rock revetment (Summary 14) to provide a fixed line of defence along the shoreline.

As a general rule, groynes should not be built on an open beach unless construction is accompanied by a commitment to regular recycling or nourishment. Without this commitment the groynes are likely to cause downdrift erosion as the upper beach becomes starved of sediment. Where there is a plentiful sediment supply, or where downdrift erosion is not considered to be a significant issue, then recycling may not be required.

Groynes should normally only be considered for beaches with a significant proportion of gravel. Structure length should extend across the full width of the steeper upper beach, allowing for beach reorientation after construction and recycling/nourishment. Further extension across the sandy lower beach is generally not effective as the sand will be transported over and around the groynes as suspended load. Groyne lengths should be reduced at the downdrift end of a series to reduce the tendency for local erosion.

Groyne spacing will depend on the nearshore direction of the dominant waves and the expected orientation of the upper beach after construction. The design of larger schemes should make use of numerical models to assess the optimum lengths and spacings.

Within estuaries groynes are used primarily to deflect tidal flows away from an eroding shoreline. To be effective structures must be large, both in elevation and lengths. Impacts can be significant on other areas of the estuary, and are difficult to predict with certainty. The services of specialist estuary consultants should be commissioned at preliminary appraisal stage.

Construction costs are mainly dependent on structure dimensions, but can be heavily influenced by the availability of suitable rock (or other material), transport and the associated costs of recycling or nourishment. Rock structures can be assumed to have an unlimited life with respect to economic assessments.

Impacts

Groynes have a significant impact on the landscape and can create barriers to the recreational use of the upper beach. They often cause downdrift erosion unless there is a long term management commitment to beach recycling or nourishment. Downdrift erosion may well lead to pressure for further defence works.

Timber groynes must be built from hardwood to endure the harsh shoreline environment. Much hardwood comes from tropical sources, making it both costly and potentially environmentally unacceptable. Timber groynes tend to reflect, rather than absorb, wave energy making them significantly less effective than rock on exposed coasts. They are also more likely to structural failure due to formation of scour channels around their seaward ends.

Best practice and environmental opportunities

Provided that groynes are used in appropriate locations, they reduce dependency on regular recycling or nourishment, and therefore reduce future disturbance of the shoreline environment. Localised accumulations of beach material will encourage new dune growth. Recycling, fencing and transplanting will help to keep the revetment sections buried, thereby enhancing habitat regeneration.

All dune management schemes should observe the following guidelines to maximise the probability of success and minimise impacts on the natural and human environment:

- Each dune erosion site must be considered independently, with management approaches tailored to the specific site.
- A policy of "Adaptive management" (Summary 1) should be considered for all sites before other options are assessed.
- Work should not be undertaken unless the beach-dune system and nearshore coastal processes have been monitored over several years and a reasonable understanding of the physical and natural environment has been established. Hasty responses to erosion may prove to be either unnecessary or damaging.
- No work of a permanent nature should be undertaken unless important immovable or irreplaceable backshore assets are at risk.
- Local interest groups, such as landowners, nature trusts, fishing associations and recreational users, should be consulted early to ensure that a broad view of the shoreline and nearshore zone is considered prior to implementing any particular management approach.
- Consideration must always be given to both long term "average" and short term extreme weather and sea conditions to determine the life expectancy of any operations.
- Consideration must be given to the consequences of failure, such as construction debris spread along the beach, public safety hazards, loss of amenity access, deterioration of the landscape, etc.
- Work should be planned and scheduled to limit damage to fragile ecosystems and to recreation. Consideration should be given to vegetation, bird nesting and migration, intertidal invertebrates, fisheries, public access, noise levels and public safety.
- All site staff must be made aware of the need for careful working practises to avoid environmental damage, and to avoid hazards associated with steep and unstable dune faces.
- Temporary or permanent management access routes to the dune face for materials, equipment and labour must be planned and constructed to minimise trampling damage to the dunes and to limit the formation of blowouts. Boardwalks or other temporary surfaces should be laid and should follow the natural contours of the dunes rather than cutting straight lines susceptible to wind erosion. Fencing should be used to stabilise sand adjacent to the track.
- Public access routes to the beach should be clearly laid out and fenced where necessary to prevent trampling that may lead to blowouts.
- Educational displays at backshore car parking areas or along footpaths should be used to explain management schemes and encourage public interest and support for the management objectives.
- Warning signs should be set up highlighting the dangers of unstable dune faces, any construction work in progress or any other hazards associated with the management schemes (gaps in rock structures, slippery algal growth, buried defences, submerged structures, mud deposits, etc)
- Post project monitoring should be undertaken at least bi-annually to assess the beach-dune evolution and the success of the scheme relative to the objectives. Appendix 2 of this guide provides monitoring guidelines.

In addition to these general guidelines, the following are of specific importance to groynes:

- Further guidance on the design of rock structures is available from the CIRIA/CUR "Manual on the use of rock in coastal and shoreline engineering" and from the CIRIA "Beach management manual".
- Groyne construction should normally be accompanied by an ongoing programme of beach recycling or nourishment. Regular monitoring and management is required to establish a successful scheme. Monitoring must include adjacent shorelines as well as those immediately within the groyne scheme.
- Groyne heights, lengths and profiles can be modified if monitoring indicates that the initial layout is not achieving the required objectives. Modification is easier to achieve with rock structures than with timber. Any observed storm damage, such as displaced rocks, should be rectified during maintenance operations.
- Timber used for groyne construction should be derived from sustainably managed forests.
- Groynes in estuaries may need navigation marks to ensure public safety.
- Where possible fencing and transplanting should be undertaken to establish a new line of foredunes along the stabilised upper beach. These dunes will enhance the coastal landscape, provide additional erosion protection and re-establish a natural succession of dune habitats from the shoreline to the backshore.
- The use of local rock should not be a requirement of design unless there are genuine landscape considerations, such as adjacent rocky outcrops; even in this instance local rock should only be used if it is readily available in the size range required and is a sound material for coastal construction.
- The use of builder's rubble is unlikely to ever be appropriate for dune management. Most material is too small to be effective and will be drawn down the beach during any significant storm. The rubble may contain material that is either hazardous to beach users, toxic or simply unattractive. Large concrete slabs may be acceptable from an engineering perspective but are unlikely to meet approval with respect to their landscape impact or their safety for use in a public area.

Summary 13: BEACH DRAINAGE

APPROPRIATE LOCATIONS	Low tidal range sand beach sites with a high amenity value, low to moderate wave energy
COSTS	Low to moderate, with high maintenance (£5,000 - £20,000/100m length, plus running costs).
EFFECTIVENESS	Increases upper beach width and therefore dune stability, variable life expectancy.
BENEFITS	Non-intrusive technique resulting in wider, drier beach
PROBLEMS	Storm erosion of beach is likely to damage the system

General description

Beach drains comprise perforated land drain pipes buried below the upper beach surface, and connected to a pump and discharge. The concept is based on the principle that sand will tend to accrete if the beach surface is permeable due to an artificially lowered water table. The system is largely buried and therefore has no visual impact.

Function

Mild upper beach and dune erosion can be controlled by beach drains. The system actively lowers the water table in the swash zone, thereby enhancing the wave absorption capacity of the beach, reducing sand fluidisation and encouraging sand deposition. The deposited sand forms an upper beach berm that protects the dune face during storm events that might otherwise cause erosion.

Benefits are greatest on micro-tidal (<2m range), high value amenity beaches where landscape issues preclude the use of other management approaches. Important backshore assets should not rely on drainage systems for erosion protection during storms, even as a temporary measure.

Active drainage systems have been found to enhance sand deposition at sites in the USA and Europe. Trial sites in the UK have had a mixed reception, partly as a result of poor site selection, inadequate design and lack of management. Installation costs can be relatively low, but maintenance and management commitments are high. Although the drains should increase upper beach volume during low to moderate wave conditions they will not be significantly effective during storms, with the result that beach draw down may lead to exposure of the pipework and system failure.

Methods

Beach drainage systems are relatively simple to install but should always be designed by a competent hydraulic consultant. Little information is available to guide designs, with the exception of that provided by organisations providing a patented installation service. In simple terms, perforated plastic drain pipes with a geotextile sleeve are laid into excavated trenches within the high tide swash zone. The pipes are connected to a pump and discharge system. Pipework must be laid at least 1m below the expected minimum beach level, but not so deep as to be ineffective at draining the surface layer of the beach. The geotextile sleeve serves to filter sand from the seawater collected in the drains. A surround of gravel has sometimes been used to improve flows. Pumping facilities must be appropriately housed and represent the major system installation and maintenance cost. Discharge of collected water should be designed to minimise any interference with natural beach processes.

Consideration must be given to the real time control of the pumping facilities. The system will only operate efficiently while the pipework is within the swash zone: at lower tide levels no wave driven sand will reach the system's area of influence, and once the still water level has risen over the drains the pumps will be overwhelmed by the total saturation of the beach. A water level sensitive pump control is therefore required, although it would also be possible to produce a time switch system based on predicted tide levels. Regular beach monitoring and system management are required to obtain optimum results from a drainage scheme.

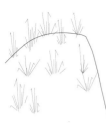

Dune face can be planted and fenced to encourage recovery. Recycling or nourishment will enhance dune growth.

Sand will accrete over the Spring tide swash zone, mainly over an area of approximately 5m-10m either side of each drain line during appropriate swash zone conditions, creating a wider upper beach

HWMOST

Perforated land drain with geotextile and gravel filter. Connected to pump and outfall system

~1m below lowest expected beach level

~10m-20m separation between parallel drains

Beach drains laid in the upper beach

The system will be most effective in areas with a low tidal range (less than 2m) in which the pump would be active for a large part of each tidal cycle. Most of the Scottish coast has a tide range of at least 3m, with a 4 - 5m range being common, so drains installed on or above high water line of the beach will be redundant for at least 75% of each year. Drainage systems will also be most effective over relatively short lengths of shoreline. A single system should be capable of achieving some benefits over lengths of 100m to 400m. Small embayments or discrete lengths of longer frontages could be appropriate sites.

Associated vegetation transplanting and fencing/thatching (Summaries 2, 3 and 4) will enhance dune growth. Beach recycling (Summary 5) may also be beneficial to the initial installation or to restoring the system if pipework is exposed by storm erosion.

Costs for drainage schemes are dependent on the number of lines laid, the problems of providing appropriate pumping and outfall facilities and the amount of maintenance required to keep the system active.

To date no information is available on which to assess life expectancy. With regular maintenance and repairs to storm damage, a system could remain active for at least 10 years before requiring a major rebuild. Sand clogging within the pipework is likely to be a limiting factor on life expectancy, assuming storm damage can be avoided.

Impacts

Construction of a drainage system will require trenching of the upper foreshore to a depth of 1m – 2m. Once installed the system should be largely invisible, although storm erosion of the upper beach may expose the pipework. Permanently visible elements will be the pump housing and discharge pipes. These may be incorporated into existing shoreline features in some instances, but will otherwise be intrusive on the landscape.

Best practice and environmental opportunities

A successful beach drainage system will increase the elevation and width of the upper beach, providing an improvement to amenity value and encouraging the formation of foredunes. The raised upper beach will provide storm protection to the dunes. Recycling or nourishment can initiate beach level increases, and fencing, thatching and transplanting can encourage dune growth.

All dune management schemes should observe the following guidelines to maximise the probability of success and minimise impacts on the natural and human environment:

- Each dune erosion site must be considered independently, with management approaches tailored to the specific site.
- A policy of "Adaptive management" (Summary 1) should be considered for all sites before other options are assessed.
- Work should not be undertaken unless the beach-dune system and nearshore coastal processes have been monitored over several years and a reasonable understanding of the physical and natural environment has been established. Hasty responses to erosion may prove to be either unnecessary or damaging.

- No work of a permanent nature should be undertaken unless important immovable or irreplaceable backshore assets are at risk.
- Local interest groups, such as landowners, nature trusts, fishing associations and recreational users, should be consulted early to ensure that a broad view of the shoreline and nearshore zone is considered prior to implementing any particular management approach.
- Consideration must always be given to both long term "average" and short term extreme weather and sea conditions to determine the life expectancy of any operations.
- Consideration must be given to the consequences of failure, such as construction debris spread along the beach, public safety hazards, loss of amenity access, deterioration of the landscape, etc.
- Work should be planned and scheduled to limit damage to fragile ecosystems and to recreation. Consideration should be given to vegetation, bird nesting and migration, intertidal invertebrates, fisheries, public access, noise levels and public safety.
- All site staff must be made aware of the need for careful working practises to avoid environmental damage, and to avoid hazards associated with steep and unstable dune faces.
- Temporary or permanent management access routes to the dune face for materials, equipment and labour must be planned and constructed to minimise trampling damage to the dunes and to limit the formation of blowouts. Boardwalks or other temporary surfaces should be laid and should follow the natural contours of the dunes rather than cutting straight lines susceptible to wind erosion. Fencing should be used to stabilise sand adjacent to the track.
- Public access routes to the beach should be clearly laid out and fenced where necessary to prevent trampling that may lead to blowouts.
- Educational displays at backshore car parking areas or along footpaths should be used to explain management schemes and encourage public interest and support for the management objectives.
- Warning signs should be set up highlighting the dangers of unstable dune faces, any construction work in progress or any other hazards associated with the management schemes (gaps in rock structures, slippery algal growth, buried defences, submerged structures, mud deposits, etc)
- Post project monitoring should be undertaken at least bi-annually to assess the beach-dune evolution and the success of the scheme relative to the objectives. Appendix 2 of this guide provides monitoring guidelines.

In addition to these general guidelines, the following are of specific importance to beach drainage:

- Trench excavation must be sufficiently deep to avoid pipework becoming exposed during storms.
- Pumping and outfall works should not be visually intrusive or impact on natural beach processes.
- Systems must be regularly monitored to ensure that pumping is optimised for greatest effect.
- If erosion continues despite the installation of a drainage system, pipework should be removed before it is exposed and damaged by storm waves.
- Where possible recycling, fencing and transplanting should be undertaken to establish a new line of foredunes to landward of the drains. These dunes will enhance the coastal landscape, provide additional erosion protection and re-establish a natural succession of dune habitats from the shoreline to the backshore.
- If the system is effective in accreting new foredunes, further lines of drain pipes should be installed and redundant lines disconnected from pumps.

Summary 14: ROCK REVETMENTS

APPROPRIATE LOCATIONS	Sites suffering severe and ongoing erosion where important and extensive backshore assets are at risk.
COSTS	High, but with relatively low maintenance (£100,000-£300,000/100m length).
EFFECTIVENESS	Good long-term protection. Can be extended or modified to allow for future shoreline change. Unlimited structure life.
BENEFITS	Low risk option for important backshore assets. Permeable face absorbs wave energy and encourages upper beach stability.
PROBLEMS	Strong landscape impact. Can alter dune system permanently as sand tends not to build up over the rocks if beach erosion continues.

General description

Rock revetments may be used to control erosion by armouring the dune face. They dissipate the energy of storm waves and prevent further recession of the backshore if well designed and maintained. Revetments may be carefully engineered structures protecting long lengths of shoreline, or roughly placed rip-rap protecting short sections of severely eroded dunes.

Major rock armour revetment in front of dune system. Though offering long-term security, the landscape impact and damage to habitat are considerable.

Function

Rock revetments are widely used in areas with important backshore assets subject to severe and ongoing erosion where it is not cost effective or environmentally acceptable to provide full protection using seawalls (Summary 16). The function of permeable revetments is to reduce the erosive power of the waves by means of wave energy dissipation in the interstices of the revetment.

Permeable revetments can also be built from gabions (Summary 8), timber (Summary 15) or concrete armour units. Concrete units are normally too costly for use as dune protection, but may be appropriate where high value back shore assets must be protected and armour rock is difficult to obtain. They are often considered to be more unattractive than rock.

Revetments may not prevent on going shoreline recession unless they are maintained, and, if necessary, extended. If the foreshore continues to erode, the rock revetment may slump down, becoming less effective as a defence structure, but will not fail completely. Repairs and extensions may be necessary to provide continued backshore protection at the design standard.

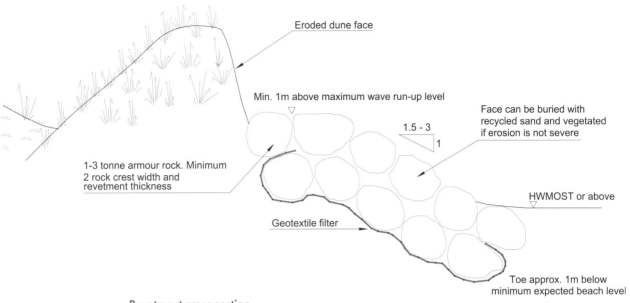

Eroded dune face

Min. 1m above maximum wave run-up level ▽

Face can be buried with recycled sand and vegetated if erosion is not severe

1.5 - 3 / 1

1-3 tonne armour rock. Minimum 2 rock crest width and revetment thickness

HWMOST or above ▽

Geotextile filter

Toe approx. 1m below minimum expected beach level

Revetment cross section

Methods

Rock revetment schemes can have a significant impact on the shoreline and should not be implemented without specialist assistance from a competent coastal consultant and contractors. Information on the design of rock structures is available from the CIRIA/CUR "Manual on the use of rock in coastal and shoreline engineering". The accompanying figures provide initial guidance but this should be confirmed for each site.

As with all rock structures on the shoreline the rock size, face slopes, crest elevation and crest width must be designed with care. Rock size is dependent on incident wave height, period and direction, structure slope, acceptance of risk, cross-sectional design, and the availability/cost of armour rock from quarries. In general 1-3 tonne rock will suffice, provided that it is placed as at least a double layer, with a 1:1.5 to 1:3 face slope, and there is an acceptance of some risk of failure. Rock size may need to increase if the beach fronting the structure is expected to drop below HWMOST.

Structure face slopes are a compromise between flatter faces that absorb more wave energy, and therefore suffer less toe scour and allow use of smaller rock, and steeper faces that give the structure a smaller footprint and require less rock volume. A slope of 1:2 is a reasonable compromise and is in keeping with natural dune slopes.

The structure should be constructed within a shallow trench and a geotextile filter should be laid under the rocks to prevent the migration of sand upwards and the settlement of the rocks into the beach. The geotextile should be wrapped around the base layer of rocks, and the rock toe should be set below the lowest expected beach level.

The length of the structure must be sufficient to protect the backshore assets at risk. To avoid localised scour the structure ends must return into the eroding dune face over the final 20m-40m and should be buried by as much as 5m-10m, depending on the expected rate of future erosion. The face slope over this final section can be flattened to 1:3 or 1:4 to increase wave absorption. The revetment length may need extending from time to time as erosion of the adjacent dune frontages may continue.

The structure crest elevation must be above the wave run-up limit during storms to prevent further dune erosion. During very extreme storms some overtopping damage will be inevitable, and the designers must determine the acceptable risk depending on potential damage and the probability of extreme events.

If the beach-revetment interface is well above normal spring tide levels there may be opportunities to use beach recycling (Summary 5), fencing and vegetation transplanting (Summaries 2 to 4) to encourage dune growth. However, as revetments are only likely to be used where erosion problems are severe, then it is unlikely that this opportunity will arise. In the latter case fencing and transplanting should be used along the structure crest to soften the landscape impact and encourage dune recovery.

Large rock revetments in areas open to the public will be a safety hazard. To increase hydraulic efficiency the rocks should be placed randomly to form a rough surface with large voids. The rocks may move when walked on and the voids may be large enough to fall or climb into, and may result in children becoming trapped or injured. Where structures extend down the shoreline below the normal spring tide levels the lower rocks will be covered by algae and other marine growth, and may be extremely slippery.

Natural recovery has allowed dunes to reform over the rock revetment. The revetment crest forms a shoreline path.

Safe access routes, usually concrete steps with hand rails, should be built at intervals across large revetments and should lead to controlled paths through the dunes. The crest of large rock revetments should be blinded, with the interstitial voids infilled with smaller rock to form a reasonable surface for safe walking. During severe storms this surface may be damaged and need maintenance to replace dislodged rocks and refill voids. In all cases the structures should be well signed to warn the public of hazards and discourage access except at controlled points.

The above discussions relate to large, engineered revetments. Less substantial defences may be formed as rip-rap slopes, but only in low energy situations. Widely graded rock from small boulders up to armour rock can be placed along estuary shores or well protected coastal sites. This approach may well be subject to regular storm damage, requiring maintenance to reform the slopes. Necessary maintenance work may well be harmful to the environment as heavy equipment will be active on the beach and may need to gain access through the dunes. Burial of the rip-rap slopes will reduce the visual impact, while fencing, thatching and transplanting may encourage covering dune growth.

Construction costs for revetments are mainly dependent on structure dimensions, but can be heavily influenced by the availability of suitable rock and transport methods. Rock structures can be assumed to have an unlimited life with respect to economic assessments, while smaller rip-rap slopes will require regular maintenance costs to be included in the budget.

Abrupt ending to rock revetment provides focus for future marine erosion, exacerbated by trampling and potential blow-out formation.

Impacts

The construction of any substantial defence along a dune face will have a significant impact on the landscape and on the natural interchange of sand between beach and dune. The natural succession of dune habitats from foredunes back to grey dunes or machair will be disrupted. Sand can be blown from the beach and over the structure to reach the dunes, but cannot be returned to counter erosion of the upper beach during storms. The consequences can be increasing shoreline recession, with the need to extend the revetment to cope with increasing wave attack. Where the revetment is built high on the beach face the erosion pressures are much reduced.

Public access will be disrupted and may be hazardous unless steps are provided.

Erosion may well continue along adjacent frontages leaving the revetment seaward of the general line of the shore and exposed to ever larger waves. Again this may necessitate on-going extension and upgrade of the defences.

Best practice and environmental opportunities

Rock revetments provide robust, long term protection for important backshore assets. The revetment crest can form a public walkway, reducing trampling of the dunes. Inclusion of safe access routes down to the beach will improve amenity value.

All dune management schemes should observe the following guidelines to maximise the probability of success and minimise impacts on the natural and human environment:

- Each dune erosion site must be considered independently, with management approaches tailored to the specific site.
- A policy of "Adaptive management" (Summary 1) should be considered for all sites before other options are assessed.
- Work should not be undertaken unless the beach-dune system and nearshore coastal processes have been monitored over several years and a reasonable understanding of the physical and natural environment has been established. Hasty responses to erosion may prove to be either unnecessary or damaging.
- No work of a permanent nature should be undertaken unless important immovable or irreplaceable backshore assets are at risk.
- Local interest groups, such as landowners, nature trusts, fishing associations and recreational users, should be consulted early to ensure that a broad view of the shoreline and nearshore zone is considered prior to implementing any particular management approach.
- Consideration must always be given to both long term "average" and short term extreme weather and sea conditions to determine the life expectancy of any operations.
- Consideration must be given to the consequences of failure, such as construction debris spread along the beach, public safety hazards, loss of amenity access, deterioration of the landscape, etc.
- Work should be planned and scheduled to limit damage to fragile ecosystems and to recreation. Consideration should be given to vegetation, bird nesting and migration, intertidal invertebrates, fisheries, public access, noise levels and public safety.
- All site staff must be made aware of the need for careful working practises to avoid environmental damage, and to avoid hazards associated with steep and unstable dune faces.
- Temporary or permanent management access routes to the dune face for materials, equipment and labour must be planned and constructed to minimise trampling damage to the dunes and to limit the formation of blowouts. Boardwalks or other temporary surfaces should be laid and should follow the natural contours of the dunes rather than cutting straight lines susceptible to wind erosion. Fencing should be used to stabilise sand adjacent to the track.
- Public access routes to the beach should be clearly laid out and fenced where necessary to prevent trampling that may lead to blowouts.
- Educational displays at backshore car parking areas or along footpaths should be used to explain management schemes and encourage public interest and support for the management objectives.
- Warning signs should be set up highlighting the dangers of unstable dune faces, any construction work in progress or any other hazards associated with the management schemes (gaps in rock structures, slippery algal growth, buried defences, submerged structures, mud deposits, etc)
- Post project monitoring should be undertaken at least bi-annually to assess the beach-dune evolution and the success of the scheme relative to the objectives. Appendix 2 of this guide provides monitoring guidelines.

In addition to these general guidelines, the following are of specific importance to rock revetments.

- Further detailed guidance on the design of rock structures is available from the CIRIA/CUR "Manual on the use of rock in coastal and shoreline engineering".
- Revetment design must anticipate ongoing erosion that may result in toe scour, overtopping or outflanking and may cause partial structural failure.
- Where possible the revetment toe should be at HWMOST or higher, and recycling, fencing and transplanting should be undertaken to establish a new line of foredunes in front of and over the revetment. These dunes will reduce visual impact, providing additional erosion protection and re-establish a natural succession of dune habitats from the shoreline to the backshore.
- Voids between armour rocks can be filled along the crest to provide a public walkway.
- Steps with handrails should be built into the revetment at intervals to provide safe public access to and from the beach.
- The use of local rock should not be a requirement of design unless there are genuine landscape considerations, such as adjacent rocky outcrops; even in this instance local rock should only be used if it is readily available in the size range required and is a sound material for coastal construction.
- The use of builder's rubble is unlikely to ever be appropriate for dune management. Most material is too small to be effective and will be drawn down the beach during any significant storm. The rubble may contain material that is either hazardous to beach users, toxic or simply unattractive. Large concrete slabs may be acceptable from an engineering perspective but are unlikely to meet approval with respect to their landscape impact or their safety for use in a public area.

Summary 15: TIMBER REVETMENTS

APPROPRIATE LOCATIONS	High value sites suffering modest and periodic erosion.
COSTS	Moderate (£2000 to £50,000/100m frontage length).
EFFECTIVENESS	Provide good protection if only occasionally exposed to waves. 5-30 year life.
BENEFITS	Normally acceptable to the public. Less expensive than seawalls or rock revetments
PROBLEMS	Limited life, particularly where exposed to wave action. Visually intrusive. Alters beach-dune processes as sand interchange is disrupted.

General description

Timber revetments can range from substantial, impermeable breastwork to temporary permeable upper beach wave barriers. The former is a final line of dune erosion protection, while the latter serves to partially dissipate wave energy before it reaches the dune face.

Timber breastwork functioning successfully within an estuary.

Function

Timber revetments have been widely used in the UK for coast protection where the costs or impacts of a seawall may have been unacceptable. Construction flexibility allows timber revetments to serve various purposes. They can provide a partial barrier to wave energy when built as a permeable "fence" along the upper beach. Alternatively they can form a final wave protection wall when built as an impermeable vertical breastwork along the dune face.

Temporary structures can be built relatively cheaply of pressure treated softwood but more substantial structures are usually built of imported hardwood. Concerns over the sustainability of hardwood sources have increased material costs considerably, making it unlikely that large scale timber defences will be used in the future. Timber is now only likely to be viable for smaller schemes in relatively low energy areas. On an open beach exposed to large storm waves, hardwood structures will be abraded, giving a life expectancy of only 15-20 years. Within estuaries or on low energy beaches the timber may last 25-30 years before abrasion and wood boring invertebrates cause significant damage. Softwood structures are likely to have a life of only 5-10 years.

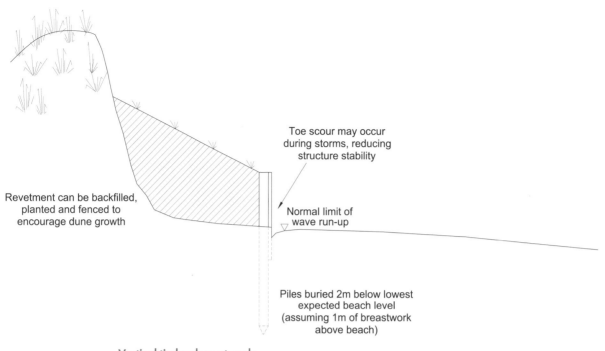

Toe scour may occur during storms, reducing structure stability

Revetment can be backfilled, planted and fenced to encourage dune growth

Normal limit of wave run-up

Piles buried 2m below lowest expected beach level (assuming 1m of breastwork above beach)

Vertical timber breastwork

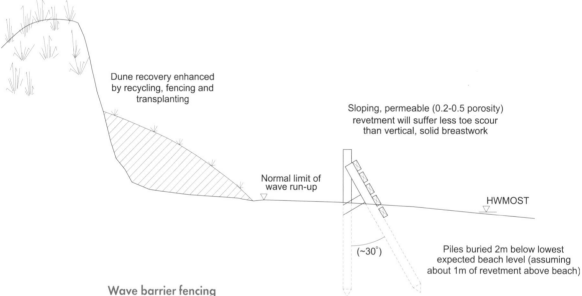

Dune recovery enhanced by recycling, fencing and transplanting

Sloping, permeable (0.2-0.5 porosity) revetment will suffer less toe scour than vertical, solid breastwork

Normal limit of wave run-up

HWMOST

(~30°)

Piles buried 2m below lowest expected beach level (assuming about 1m of revetment above beach)

Wave barrier fencing

Methods

The flexibility of timber as a construction material allows designers to exercise their imaginations, provided that a few basic principles are be observed: two possible designs are illustrated above. Small schemes with short design life can be put in place without specialist skills, but larger schemes intended to last more than a few years require the services of competent coastal engineers and contractors. At the most basic level timber revetments may be little more than the dune fences discussed in Summary 4.

Structures built within the active beach zone must be designed to withstand wave impacts and changing beach levels. Support piles must be well buried to prevent rotational failure, particularly when beach levels drop during storms. All fixings must take account of the corrosive marine environment and must be secure against vandalism. Public access routes across the structures must be built in to the design.

Timber breastwork should be built above the limit of normal wave run up. Impermeable vertical structures built lower on the foreshore will suffer toe scour and may be undermined causing collapse. Recycling, fencing and transplanting in front of the breastwork will reduce the landscape impact and enhance the dune-beach interactions and habitats. Straight, shore parallel structures are likely to provide adequate service. More complex layouts (see photo) may offer some minor advantages in terms of encouraging dune recovery, but are unlikely to be as effective as a well designed and managed straight breast work with a programme of fencing and transplanting.

Local scour at the ends of the breastwork can be reduced by feathering the structure back into the dune face over a distance of 20m to 40m. A short length of rock armour revetment extending off the end of the timber may be beneficial if erosion is expected to be severe.

Timber wave barriers can be built lower on the foreshore, but should still be above HWMOST. They should be designed to reduce wave energy reaching the upper beach, allowing greater upper beach stability and therefore dune face stability. Structure porosity (spaces : solid) should be in the region of 0.2 to 0.5. Wave barriers can be vertical or sloping, though sloping structures are more likely to remain stable under wave impacts.

The approximate limits of wave run-up can be established by observing and recording the location of the strand line over Spring tide periods during both winter storms and more normal wave conditions. The toe of a freshly eroded dune face is normally just below the run-up limit of the most recent severe sea.

Costs for timber revetments are dependent on design, dimensions, quality of materials and the requirement for skilled contractors. Life expectancy will range from a few years up to 30 years, depending on rates of shoreline erosion, cross-shore location of structures and quality of timber.

Impacts

In common with all fixed dune face structures, solid revetments or breastwork disrupt the natural interchange of sand between dunes and beaches with the loss of the succession of habitats from foredunes back to the stable grey dunes or machairs. Sand can be blown from the beach and over the structures to reach the dunes, but cannot be returned to counter erosion of the beach during storms. The consequences can be increasing shoreline recession, with the exposure of the piles leading to ultimate structural failure. Similarly, on-going erosion of adjacent unprotected dunes may result in outflanking necessitating extension of defences. Where the revetment is built high on the beach face the erosion pressures are much reduced.

Permeable wave barrier revetments are less disruptive of natural processes as they allow a continued interchange of sand from beach to dune. Used appropriately they can be beneficial to dune protection over a time scale of 5-20 years. They are also more intrusive on the coastal landscape as they are built on the active upper beach and will not be covered by dunes.

Both types of structures will impact on recreational use of the beach, and must include appropriate access routes.

Recently built timber and geotextile breastwork.

Best practice and environmental opportunities

Timber structures offer great flexibility in design. They can be incorporated into recreation management schemes and are often readily accepted by the public. Timber structure are easily repaired or extended relative to concrete structures.

All dune management schemes should observe the following guidelines to maximise the probability of success and minimise impacts on the natural and human environment:

- Each dune erosion site must be considered independently, with management approaches tailored to the specific site.
- A policy of "Adaptive management" (Summary 1) should be considered for all sites before other options are assessed.
- Work should not be undertaken unless the beach-dune system and nearshore coastal processes have been monitored over several years and a reasonable understanding of the physical and natural environment has been established. Hasty responses to erosion may prove to be either unnecessary or damaging.
- No work of a permanent nature should be undertaken unless important immovable or irreplaceable backshore assets are at risk.
- Local interest groups, such as landowners, nature trusts, fishing associations and recreational users, should be consulted early to ensure that a broad view of the shoreline and nearshore zone is considered prior to implementing any particular management approach.
- Consideration must always be given to both long term "average" and short term extreme weather and sea conditions to determine the life expectancy of any operations.
- Consideration must be given to the consequences of failure, such as construction debris spread along the beach, public safety hazards, loss of amenity access, deterioration of the landscape, etc.
- Work should be planned and scheduled to limit damage to fragile ecosystems and to recreation. Consideration should be given to vegetation, bird nesting and migration, intertidal invertebrates, fisheries, public access, noise levels and public safety.
- All site staff must be made aware of the need for careful working practises to avoid environmental damage, and to avoid hazards associated with steep and unstable dune faces.
- Temporary or permanent management access routes to the dune face for materials, equipment and labour must be planned and constructed to minimise trampling damage to the dunes and to limit the formation of blowouts. Boardwalks or other temporary surfaces should be laid and should follow the natural contours of the dunes rather than cutting straight lines susceptible to wind erosion. Fencing should be used to stabilise sand adjacent to the track.
- Public access routes to the beach should be clearly laid out and fenced where necessary to prevent trampling that may lead to blowouts.
- Educational displays at backshore car parking areas or along footpaths should be used to explain management schemes and encourage public interest and support for the management objectives.
- Warning signs should be set up highlighting the dangers of unstable dune faces, any construction work in progress or any other hazards associated with the management schemes (gaps in rock structures, slippery algal growth, buried defences, submerged structures, mud deposits, etc)
- Post project monitoring should be undertaken at least bi-annually to assess the beach-dune evolution and the success of the scheme relative to the objectives. Appendix 2 of this guide provides monitoring guidelines.

In addition to these general guidelines, the following are of specific importance to timber revetments:

- Design must anticipate ongoing shoreline erosion that may result in undermining, overtopping or outflanking, causing structural failure.
- Where possible recycling, fencing and transplanting should be undertaken to establish a new line of foredunes in front of and over the revetment. These dunes will reduce visual impact, providing additional erosion protection and re-establishing a natural succession of dune habitats from the shoreline to the backshore.
- Hardwood timber should be harvested from sustainably managed forests.
- Damage should be repaired rapidly to maintain the effectiveness of the scheme.

Summary 16: IMPERMEABLE REVETMENTS AND SEAWALLS

Appropriate locations	Exposed frontages with extensive and high value backshore assets.
Costs	High, but low maintenance (£200,000 - £500,000/100m length).
Effectiveness	Provides good medium term protection, but continued erosion will cause long term failure (30-50 year life expectancy).
Benefits	Fixed line of defences allowing development up to shoreline. Allows amenity facilities along backshore and easy access to beach.
Problems	Continued erosion may cause undermining and structural failure. Complete disruption of natural beach-dune processes.

General description

Impermeable revetments are continuous sloping defence structures of concrete or stone blockwork, asphalt or mass concrete. Revetments are built along the dune face, preferably above the run-up limit of waves under normal conditions. Where frequent wave attack is anticipated, the revetment may be topped by a vertical or recurved wall to reduce overtopping.

Seawalls are near vertical structures of concrete, masonry or sheet piles, designed to withstand severe wave attack. Their use was popular in the past but they are now normally considered to be costly, detrimental to the stability of beaches and unsuitable for erosion management along a dune shoreline.

Rock faced concrete revetment with sheet piled toe and rock armour apron. The rock armour was placed after beach lowering exposed the toe of the revetment. The good medium term protection of such structures has to be balanced against considerable landscape impact and habitat damage.

Function

Impermeable revetments provide a fixed line of defence for frontages with high value backshore assets. They are intended to withstand storm wave attack over a life expectancy of 30 to 50 years. Amenity facilities such as promenades, slipways and beach access steps can be built into the revetment.

Revetments will severely disrupt natural beach-dune interactions, and should not be used on frontages valued for natural heritage. Ongoing beach erosion may result in undermining of the revetment toe, leading eventually to structural failure or the need for repairs and extensions.

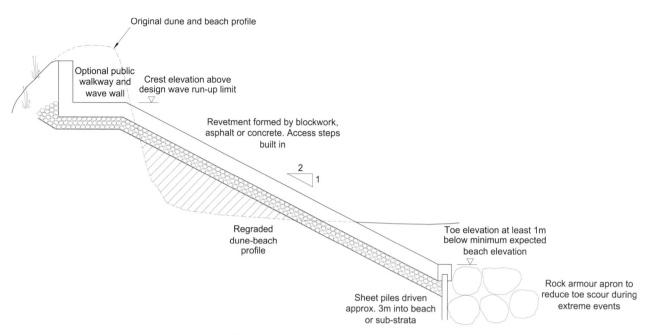

Original dune and beach profile

Optional public walkway and wave wall

Crest elevation above design wave run-up limit

Revetment formed by blockwork, asphalt or concrete. Access steps built in

2
1

Regraded dune-beach profile

Toe elevation at least 1m below minimum expected beach elevation

Rock armour apron to reduce toe scour during extreme events

Sheet piles driven approx. 3m into beach or sub-strata

Typical impermeable revetment cross-section

Methods

The design and construction of impermeable revetments and seawalls requires the services of competent coastal engineers and contractors. Guidance is available from various publications, including "Coastal Protection" (Pilarczyk, 1990), "Designing Seawalls" (Thomas and Hall, 1992) and "Revetment systems against wave attack – A Design Manual" (McConnell, 1998). The figure above indicates a typical revetment cross-section, but design must be site specific.

Revetments should have a sloping face extending well below the normal beach level to allow for future foreshore erosion. Sheet piles at the toe should be driven down into the substrata to provide structural support and prevent leaching of sediment out from under the revetment. Rock armour placed in front of the sheet piles will provide additional support and reduce the potential for future toe scour in the event of ongoing foreshore erosion. The revetment crest should be set according to expected wave run-up levels, and can be topped by a vertical wave wall if further backshore protection is required. The crest elevation will be higher than required for a rock revetment as the structure will suffer greater wave run-up over the smooth and impermeable surface. A promenade can be added along the crest to reduce public pressure on the backshore dunes.

Structure face slopes are a compromise between flatter faces that absorb more wave energy, and therefore suffer less scour, and steeper faces that give the structure a smaller foot print and lower construction cost. A slope of 1:2 is a reasonable compromise, and is in keeping with the natural dune slope. Increasing surface roughness will make little difference to hydraulic performance, but may increase potential for blown sand to stabilise on the structure face. Increasing porosity is possible and effective, but the additional construction costs are unlikely to be justified for dune protection.

The face must be able to withstand impact and uplift forces during storms. Where blockwork is used the units must interlock or otherwise connect to form a unified surface, as the loss of a single unit will cause rapid deterioration of the whole structure. A sound foundation of geotextile and a crushed rock bedding layer will reduce the potential for damage due to hydraulic forces acting from below the revetment face.

Continued dune face erosion should be anticipated along adjacent frontages. The terminal ends of the revetment should be feathered smoothly back to the dune face, to prevent local scour from outflanking the structure. Feathering can be achieved using rock armour over the final 20m to 40m of the defence length line, with the rocks running back into the dune face to a depth of 5m to 10m depending on the anticipated rate of future erosion. Rocks can be placed at a flatter slope (1:3 or 1:4) to increase wave absorption.

Public beach access routes should be incorporated into the structure, linked to backshore walkways or a promenade along the crest. If the revetment face extends below normal spring tide level the surface may become coated with slippery algae, creating a public hazard. Appropriate hand rails or improved footings will be required for safe walking.

In favourable circumstances sand may build up along the revetment face, providing an opportunity to use recycling, fencing and vegetation (Summaries 2 to 5) to stabilise a new line of foredunes. These dunes will enhance the landscape and provide additional erosion protection, but may also have a detrimental impact on backshore amenity as blown sand may block access routes, roads, car parks, etc.

Costs for impermeable revetments and seawalls vary according to the type of construction, required dimensions, anticipated rates of future erosion, backshore facilities such as walkways and amenity add ons such as steps or slipways. Economic assessment should assume a life expectancy of up to 50 years before major repairs or reconstruction will be required.

Sloping open stone asphalt wall with rock apron.

Impacts

In common with all fixed dune face structures, revetments disrupt the natural interchange of sand between dunes and beaches with the loss of the succession from foredunes back to the stable grey dunes or machair. Sand can be blown from the beach and over the structure to reach the dunes, but cannot be returned to counter erosion of the beach during storms. The consequences can be increasing shoreline recession, with the exposure of the revetment toe leading to ultimate structural failure. Impacts may be felt along adjacent frontages that may become starved of sediment input, leading to further erosion and the demand for extended defences. Where the revetment is built high on the beach face the erosion pressures are much reduced.

Concrete and stone seawall. In common with many other fixed structures the natural interchange of sand between beach and dunes is prevented with the consequent loss of transitional habitats.

Best practice and environmental opportunities

Revetments can be used to provide safe public access to the beach, and can support a promenade along the shoreline that may reduce the trampling of the remaining dunes. The backshore can be protected from marine erosion and a grey dune habitat can be maintained.

All dune management schemes should observe the following guidelines to maximise the probability of success and minimise impacts on the natural and human environment:

- Each dune erosion site must be considered independently, with management approaches tailored to the specific site.
- A policy of "Adaptive management" (Summary 1) should be considered for all sites before other options are assessed.
- Work should not be undertaken unless the beach-dune system and nearshore coastal processes have been monitored over several years and a reasonable understanding of the physical and natural environment has been established. Hasty responses to erosion may prove to be either unnecessary or damaging.
- No work of a permanent nature should be undertaken unless important immovable or irreplaceable backshore assets are at risk.
- Local interest groups, such as landowners, nature trusts, fishing associations and recreational users, should be consulted early to ensure that a broad view of the shoreline and nearshore zone is considered prior to implementing any particular management approach.
- Consideration must always be given to both long term "average" and short term extreme weather and sea conditions to determine the life expectancy of any operations.
- Consideration must be given to the consequences of failure, such as construction debris spread along the beach, public safety hazards, loss of amenity access, deterioration of the landscape, etc.
- Work should be planned and scheduled to limit damage to fragile ecosystems and to recreation. Consideration should be given to vegetation, bird nesting and migration, intertidal invertebrates, fisheries, public access, noise levels and public safety.
- All site staff must be made aware of the need for careful working practises to avoid environmental damage, and to avoid hazards associated with steep and unstable dune faces.
- Temporary or permanent management access routes to the dune face for materials, equipment and labour must be planned and constructed to minimise trampling damage to the dunes and to limit the formation of blowouts. Boardwalks or other temporary surfaces should be laid and should follow the natural contours of the dunes rather than cutting straight lines susceptible to wind erosion. Fencing should be used to stabilise sand adjacent to the track.
- Public access routes to the beach should be clearly laid out and fenced where necessary to prevent trampling that may lead to blowouts.
- Educational displays at backshore car parking areas or along footpaths should be used to explain management schemes and encourage public interest and support for the management objectives.
- Warning signs should be set up highlighting the dangers of unstable dune faces, any construction work in progress or any other hazards associated with the management schemes (gaps in rock structures, slippery algal growth, buried defences, submerged structures, mud deposits, etc)
- Post project monitoring should be undertaken at least bi-annually to assess the beach-dune evolution and the success of the scheme relative to the objectives. Appendix 2 of this guide provides monitoring guidelines.

In addition to these general guidelines, the following are of specific importance to impermeable revetments:

- Revetment design must anticipate ongoing erosion that may result in toe scour, overtopping, outflanking and leaching of underlying sediment, each of which may cause structural failure.
- Where possible recycling, fencing and transplanting should be undertaken to establish a new line of foredunes in front of and over the revetment. These dunes will reduce visual impact, providing additional erosion protection and re-establishing a natural succession of dune habitats from the shoreline to the backshore.
- Steps with handrails should be built into the revetment at intervals to provide safe public access to and from the beach.

Summary 17: NOVEL COAST PROTECTION METHODS

Dumping of rubble is unsightly, poses a health hazard and does little to impede natural shoreline recession.

There are a number of coast protection techniques that are of marginal use for dune protection. They are either unproven or inappropriate. These include the following:

- Open revetments or breastwork
- Artificial seaweed
- Seaweed planting
- Bubble barriers
- Alternative breakwaters
- Sunken vessels
- Tyre revetments
- Interlinked concrete block mattresses
- Bitumen spraying

Open revetments, sills or breastwork

Large rocks, concrete tank traps or timber "soldiers" (vertical piles) placed at discrete intervals in a line or as an open array along the mid to upper beach will have a limited influence on cross-shore wave energy. During mild conditions they may have a positive impact on upper beach and dune stability, but their impact during storms may be negligible. As the units are brought closer together to form a tight array they begin to act as a standard permeable headland, breakwater, reef or revetment (Summaries 9, 11, 12 and 14) and become increasingly effective at damping wave energy. To achieve storm protection a void to solid ratio of 0.3 – 0.5 would be required, preferably with a cross-shore width of at least two units (e.g. 2 rows of touching rocks). A properly designed structure would also have the advantage of greater stability of individual elements (i.e. single rocks or concrete units on the beach are less stable than rocks forming a structure).

Artificial seaweed

There have been several attempts at placing artificial seaweed mats in the nearshore zone in an effort to decrease wave energy by the process of frictional drag. The field trials have generally been inconclusive as regards wave energy attenuation. The most successful trials have been in areas of very low wave conditions, low tide range and relatively constant tidal current flows, when some sedimentation was found to take place.

On open coast sites there have been major problems with the installation of the systems and the synthetic seaweed fronds have shown very little durability even under modest wave attack. The synthetic seaweed has tended to flatten under wave action, thereby having minimal impact upon waves approaching the coast.

Field trials in the United Kingdom have been unsuccessful and the experiments were abandoned in all cases, due to the material being ripped away from the anchorage points.

In the Netherlands experiments were more successful with synthetic seaweed being placed in relatively deep water, where sedimentation up to 0.35m took place soon after installation, although this would result in only a very minor decrease in shoreline wave conditions.

The cost of the artificial seaweed is low but the costs and frequency of maintenance works make this option not worth pursuing in an exposed coastal environment, where it would be subject to severe wave conditions and would become damaged rapidly.

Seaweed planting

Seaweed planting can be considered as an alternative to the installation of synthetic seaweed, and works on the same principle of dissipating wave energy by friction. Artificial planting of Posidonia in relatively protected water is now well understood. However there are problems with applying this technique in open coastlines including growth time and creating sufficient plant area. The technique is unproven as far as the significant damping of open coast waves and is unlikely to be of use in dune management.

Bubble barriers

The principle behind the bubble barrier technique is the creation of a continuous curtain of bubbles rising from the seabed to dampen wave energy. The concept was developed with the aim of stilling wave energy at the mouths of harbours, where it would be possible to create suitable conditions over a short distance. The installation costs of such techniques are high, and the maintenance problems are likely to be difficult.

The bubble barrier technique is inappropriate for an open coast location where the costs of installation over hundreds of metres or greater would be considerable. The technique is still very much in an experimental stage with respect to shore protection.

Alternative breakwaters

A considerable amount of research has been carried out on the potential performance of various types of breakwater including:

- Layered plate frameworks
- Floating breakwaters
- Perforated caissons

These techniques involve the attenuation of wave energy by means other than providing a direct barrier. The numerous designs that have been tested or built are usually specific to a particular wave environment, and are usually aimed at vessel protection over relatively short distance. Design, construction and management costs are high. None have been shown to be practical as far as dune protection is concerned.

Sunken vessels

Another method of shoreline protection involves the placement of vessel hulks parallel to the shoreline to dissipate incoming wave energy. Parts of the east coast of the UK are fringed by marshes and these are particularly sensitive to changes in the wave climate, changed sediment supply, etc. On the borders of the Dengie peninsula at the mouth of the Thames Estuary there are extensive salt marshes affected by erosion. Attempts have been made to create conditions conducive to regeneration of salt marsh growth by grounding a line of barge hulks several hundred metres off the shore on shallow mud flats.

The cost of protection is relatively low and few maintenance costs are attached to this form of protection. However, this method does not easily lend itself to the protection of dune systems, if only because of the various adverse impacts that may be encountered. The hulks act like a series of breakwaters, having a strong influence on coastal processes. Not only is wave energy dissipated, but littoral transport is strongly affected. The inability to fine tune such structures means that the adverse impacts down coast may be as severe as any local beneficial impacts, in terms of protection, that are achievable. The hulks are also very intrusive on the coastal landscape and may be unstable under the high wave energy conditions found off many Scottish dune systems.

Tyre revetments

Because of the availability of scrap tyres a number of trials have been undertaken in the U.S.A. to use them as low cost shoreline protection. Much of the shoreline in the U.S.A. is in private ownership, hence there is a need for the development of solutions utilising cheap materials and simple to construct installation methods.

The intended function is to dissipate wave energy by means of the porosity characteristics of the tyre structures. This is by no means easily achievable due to problems with holding tyres together adequately.

This system is not recommended for any but very sheltered conditions. Even then, scrap tyres cannot be recommended for general use. Tests made in the U.S.A. categorised the wave height range under which tyres could be used, as being below 2 feet (less than 0.6m). The main problem is that individual tyres are much stronger than the interconnections between them.

A revetment constructed of scrap tyres will be visually intrusive. The tyres are almost indestructible hence there is a potential for adding a highly unattractive element to the shoreline if they were to come loose.

Inter-linked concrete block revetments

Patented concrete block mattress systems are widely used for protecting estuary and river banks, and for protecting the face of earth embankments. The individual blocks are linked to form flexible mattress, often using flexible cables, allowing large surface area to be covered rapidly.

None of these mattresses are suitable for use as dune face protection in situations where wave attack is experienced. They require a well laid and compacted base to prevent hydraulic uplift forces from buckling the mattress, and they require solid fixing at the crest, toe and ends to prevent slumping or outflanking. Neither of these criteria can be met in most dune situations. At best they can be used as a costly temporary structure.

Bitumen spraying

Various surface stabilising sprays, including bitumen, have been trialed in the UK and elsewhere with the aim of reducing wind erosion of dunes,. The sprays temporarily fix the dune surface and allow newly transplanted grasses to become rooted if they are placed in very mobile sand. Any surface distribution (i.e. trampling or wave attack) will quickly break through the surface layer leaving the sand in its original form.

This approach may have some benefit to backshore blowout management, but will have little, if any, benefit to an eroding seaward face.

Appendix 2 Monitoring erosion and change in dune systems

1 Introduction

Managing a beach-dune system effectively requires data on the initial character of the system, changes over a range of timescales and the factors which cause change. The data is required to:

- identify and understand change
- guide the planning of management operations
- appraise the performance and impacts of management.

There are several steps required to develop a useful database. A desk study must be completed to determine what information exists already, a baseline survey must be undertaken to establish the situation against which future change will be compared, and a programme of ongoing monitoring must be implemented to assess change and guide future management.

The desk study should include a review of maps, aerial photographs, surveys, published reports (see References) and any other documents that may reveal information relating to the past evolution of the shoreline, possibly including records of storms, shoreline construction works or periods of intense human activities impacting on the dunes (e.g. military exercises, sand mining, grazing). This information will help in understanding the present and may guide the monitoring programme.

The baseline survey will establish the existing physical character of the beach and dunes. It should be as detailed as possible and may take at least a year to complete.

Ongoing monitoring will include a subset of the baseline measurements and may include surveys at a range of different frequencies (e.g. hourly water levels, monthly walkover observations, seasonal profiling, annual aerial photography, five-yearly bathymetric surveys). The monitoring programme must be appropriate to the site, cost effective, flexible and must provide the amount and quality of data required by the shoreline manager.

Monitoring can help determine whether erosion is cyclical or part of a long-term trend. The progressive exposure of this outfall, originally sited flush with the dune face, reflects on-going erosion of over 1m per year.

This appendix sets out the reasons for monitoring, suggests what should be measured, measurement methods and frequencies, approaches to analysis and discusses management responses. The methods include details of simple, low cost approaches and general guidance on more specialist techniques. It is assumed that shoreline managers will turn to competent consultants and contractors if there is a requirement to use specialist techniques. The appendix only covers monitoring of physical characteristics and does not cover any biological or social monitoring approaches, although these may be equally important to the planning and implementation of a dune-beach management programme.

2 Aims and objectives for monitoring

Monitoring must be driven by the need to provide appropriate data for shoreline management. There are several stages in this process:

- Understanding the past: short term fluctuations and long term trends in dune-beach evolution need to be identified to understand the present and predict the future.
- Identifying potential problems: monitoring allows significant change to be identified so that a reasoned response can be developed and implemented, for example, if dune erosion may lead to damage to an important backshore asset.
- Predicting the future: past and recent developments along the shoreline are a guide to the future evolution.
- Monitoring management operations: feedback on beach-dune response to operations will guide future management, possibly suggesting refinements or alternatives.

3 Priorities for measurement

Each site will have specific aspects that require initial measurement and ongoing monitoring. In general the level of risk to fixed backshore assets will control the level of monitoring. Potential loss of footpaths, rough grazing or low value amenity areas may only justify investment in occasional visits by management staff to observe or photograph changes to the dune face. At the other end of the risk scale are high value assets such as industrial facilities or residential developments. For these sites it may well be worth developing a programme of accurate, frequent and high resolution measurements, including installation of wave/tide gauges and meteorological equipment, commissioning of topographic surveys and aerial photography, and development of computerised data storage and analysis systems. The possibilities for measurement will almost always exceed the budget, so priorities must be set.

The following are presented in their likely order of priority for baseline measurement and ongoing monitoring of an open coast situation:

- Dune face position, rate and lateral extent of erosion, rate of dune recovery following erosion, and variability of upper beach levels.
- Sediment distribution and variability, both spatially and temporally.
- Water levels, nearshore waves and winds.
- Geomorphology and ongoing evolution of adjacent cliffs, underlying foreshore strata and nearshore seabed features.
- Evolution of backshore dunes.
- Nearshore currents (more important in and around estuaries).
- Variation in backshore groundwater levels.

These priorities do not include biological or social monitoring, although these may be equally important to the selection, planning and implementation of a management programme.

4 Frequency, timing and location of measurements

Dunes and beaches evolve continually in response to waves, water levels, winds, human activities, biological processes, etc. Rates of change vary from the micro-scale of wave periods, through tidal cycles, up to seasons and beyond to decades. Micro-scales are of little practical significance to dune management, so the most obvious changes will be as a result of storms (one or two days) or seasons (winter to summer). These relatively short term changes may mask the longer term evolution over decades. It is important that dune monitoring recognises these different scales. Baseline measurements must establish the existing situation, including the potential short-term variability of that situation. Once variability is understood, monitoring can concentrate on longer-term trends.

For example, water levels change continuously and the upper beach levels will change with every tide, while the position of the dune toe may only change during storms. Establishing astronomical tidal elevations requires several measurements per hour over a period of at least one month using self-recording equipment. Establishing the baseline for the upper beach may require frequent observations and elevation surveys every month for a year to define an envelope of variability. The baseline for the dune toe may require quarterly and post-storm surveys. Subsequent monitoring of the beach and dune face might both relax to twice yearly, while tide levels will not need to be measured again (continuous monitoring would reveal storm surges and allow predictions of extremes, but this is unlikely to be required for most dune management operations).

The timing of some measurements is also important, particularly with respect to beach profile monitoring. If the intention is to measure the extremes of variability, surveys should be completed during or immediately after severe storms, when beaches will be drawn down, and also during periods of prolonged light swell and longshore winds when both beach and dune face are likely to be fully recovered. However, if the intention is to establish long term trends, the surveys should be undertaken when sea conditions are likely to show some consistency. For example, the monitoring programme might call for beach profiles to be completed within two days of the peak Spring tides of every second month – this would allow seasonal variations to be established and year on year trends to be identified with minimal observer bias.

Location of each measurement must be considered for the same reasons as timing. Establishing trends requires the surveyor to measure the same points or profiles on each occasion. Changes of even a few metres alongshore in the location of a beach-dune profile may introduce uncertainty into the analysis, particularly if there are any distinct features on the beach such as rock outcrops, streams or structures. Alternatively, if the surveyor wishes to establish potential variability during the baseline study, it may be preferable to shift profiles or point measurements by a small distance to record extremes of change, such as an area of maximum dune recovery or a scour channel caused by unusual wave induced currents.

5 Monitoring techniques – low cost approaches

5.1 Introduction

Dune systems are three-dimensional and irregular in form and do not lend themselves easily to analysis by standard surveying techniques. A set of x,y,z co-ordinates tells little about the health or evolution of a dune system, while a comparison of a number of such surveys to determine annual changes may be extremely difficult because of the very irregular and dynamic nature of a dune field. When managing a dune system a simple evaluation of the approximate extent and frequency of marine erosion or accretion is more important than an evaluation of the detailed volumes. This section directs the shoreline manager towards simple but effective techniques for monitoring using tape measures and cameras. Simple surveying equipment, such as levels or Total Stations, can be used for the same purposes if available, but this will require some additional training in field methods and data processing.

Erosion of the frontal dunes often manifests itself as a distinct scarp line that is easily identified if the dune/beach system is examined in cross-section. Changes over time to this cross-section, and the lateral extent of change, will provide useful information about the dune evolution. If the scarping is localised then the erosional processes must also be localised, possibly a funnelling of wave energy due to the construction of groynes, breakwaters or a revetment. If the scarping is widespread within an estuary then erosion may be due to a realignment of tidal flow channels. The intensity of erosion can clearly be related to the height of the scarp relative to the total height of the dunes and to the area of sand eroded to form that scarp. In terms of evaluating dune evolution a combination of techniques is necessary to locate the erosion or accretion areas, quantify the extent of damage, determine the likely causes and to evaluate the rate of change.

5.2 Establishing beach zones

Ideally, management operations require knowledge of tidal elevations, the extent of wave run-up under normal conditions and the potential maximum extent of run-up during storms. If data from a local tide gauge has been analysed to establish astronomical tidal characteristics (Highest Astronomical Tide, High Water Mark Ordinary Spring Tide, etc.), these can be related to an Ordnance Survey bench mark and used to establish beach face positions. However, in most locations around Scotland local tide data will not be available and the beaches may well be remote from any Ordnance Survey control. In these situation dune management must rely on interpretation of observations.

Seaweed and other flotsam will be left as a strand line along the upper beach after each high tide. Regular observations of the position of the strand line can be used to establish appropriate locations for any dune management schemes. The strand line is determined by the combined effect of the tidal elevation and wave run-up. The normal limit of wave run-up under high Spring tides, assuming moderate wave conditions, will define the seaward limit of shoreline vegetation. Foredunes will begin to form to landward of this line, but can easily be destroyed during storms.

The limit of storm wave run-up on an eroding beach will be defined by the elevation and position of the erosion scarp toe, though waves may actually splash even further up the face. Marram grass will not survive within this storm inundation area and therefore makes a useful indicator of the maximum run-up limit. Lyme grass and sand couch grass will survive occasional inundation and may grow further down the dune face.

Occasional extreme events, combining a storm surge water level and severe wave conditions, will cause run-up and erosion even further up the dune face. The potential importance of defining these extremes depends on the level of risk acceptable at the site. Sites with important and valuable backshore assets may need to be protected by substantial defences, and the services of specialist consultants will be required to establish appropriate design conditions.

5.3   Locating erosion areas

A reconnaissance survey should be made to identify obvious signs of dune retreat or areas of wind blown erosion (blow-outs). Sketches should be made on an Ordnance Survey map at 1:2500. Local topographic features such as footpaths, field boundaries, coppices or planted woodland should be used to provide an approximate indication of the location and extent of the eroded area. Details of the conditions in that area should be set out on a proforma, an example of which is attached. It is important to note the presence of any man-made features such as groynes, seawalls, outfalls, etc. as all of these could contribute to dune instability. Signs of trampling by livestock or by man should also be recorded.

Monitoring of reprofiled dune face with simple levelling equipment.

Fixed aspect photographs should be taken from features which are easily identifiable so that repeat monitoring can be carried out (all photos must be dated and annotated to provide a meaningful record). Photos should show the dune crest, face and toe in profile, plus any other interesting features observed during the visit. The location of the photographer's position should be noted and, if possible, clearly marked on site to allow re-establishment on subsequent visits.

At this stage it is worth setting up several markers to be used as datums for subsequent surveys. Marker posts should ideally be made of 2m long pressure treated timber posts (60mm diameter) or scaffold pipe driven at least 1m into the beach at about 50m intervals along the toe of the dunes; the spacing may be greater for systems with uniform alongshore features or less for smaller or more complex systems. Another line of markers should be set out 30m or so landwards of the first line in positions that are safe from erosion. The posts should be located as accurately as possible on a 1:2500 OS map, with the landward set intended to be used to reposition the beach posts if they are lost. The distance and bearing from one to the other must be noted along with position relative to adjacent sets of markers or fixed points within the dunes (pill boxes, fences, trees, etc). Each marker must have a unique reference. Figures A1 and A2 illustrate the set up of marker posts.

Surveys can be conducted in two ways. The simplest approach, applicable to small dune systems with minor erosion problems, is to hand measure offsets from the marker posts using a 50m fabric tape and a compass. The distance and bearing to the dune toe, the highwater line and to other distinguishable features (berms, spits, trash lines etc.) should be measured. A simple spreadsheet can be used to plot and analyse repeat surveys. Where available a simple surveyor's level with stadia lines can be used effectively by a two person team with very limited training. Elevations and distances relative to a fixed point can be recorded rapidly and accurately (+/-2mm vertically, +/-200mm horizontally).

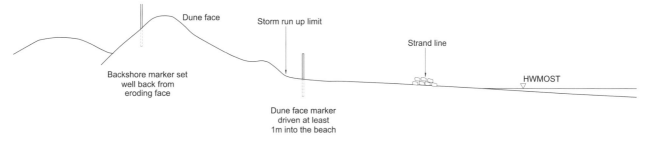

Figure A1   Dune profile showing possible locations for markers

More extensive dune systems with important backshore assets at risk should be surveyed in greater detail. A Total Station can be used to survey profiles by a competent dune manager and an assistant after limited training. Cross-shore profiles from the grey dunes down to the low water mark can be measured relative to a line defined by a pair of well-established marker posts of known position and elevation. Survey lines should generally be approximately shore normal to limit the complexity of analysis. Spacings of 50m to 100m should be sufficient to define changes along the dune system, with small bays and estuaries requiring closer spacing than extensive open coast systems

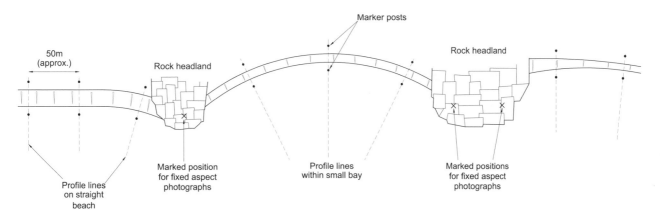

Figure A2   Plan of dune face showing possible profile line layouts

Assistance from a trained surveyor may be required to establish the control marker positions and elevations accurately, but follow on surveys can be undertaken by a team of two non-specialist personnel. Results can be plotted, stored and analysed using a simple spreadsheet, or more complex survey analysis software (Section 5.2 below).

Hand held GPS (Global Positioning System) equipment is not yet sufficiently accurate to allow for adequate surveying, although future developments may alter this view. Differential GPS can be very accurate but will certainly require the services of trained surveyors.

5.4   Equipment

Once the marker posts have been fixed the minimum required survey equipment is simple and portable, requiring only one person (although it is recommended that two people work together for speed and safety, particularly in remote locations):

- 50m fabric tape measure
- hand held clinometer to measure slopes
- camera with date stamp (digital or print film), always use same lens and focal length (if variable)
- note book/monitoring proforma (example included)
- hand held navigation compass.

Improved data can be obtained using a simple surveyor's level or a Total Station to replace the tape and clinometer. The cost of staff training and the additional time spent setting up, processing data and transporting equipment may not be justified for many sites.

If marker posts are displaced (by waves, livestock or people) they must be carefully re-established and their new position noted. Markers used for Total Station Surveys should be re-surveyed relative to each other during every field operation. This does not take long and ensures that analysis will be based on a valid datum.

5.5   Determining the likely causes of erosion

Having mapped out the erosion areas some preliminary evaluation should be made as to the likely causes of erosion. Wind data can be purchased from the nearest anemometer station and any periods of high winds from the main onshore wave generating directions highlighted. Records from the nearest tide gauge station should be examined for any periods of higher than normal water levels. This simple data review should reveal the recent periods of likely dune erosion.

If the records fail to identify any such events, other reasons for erosion should be considered. Natural reasons for dune toe erosion should be obvious from the site inspection. For example, the undercutting of the dune foot by meandering tidal channels within an estuary should be evident. If erosion has been caused by man, and is of a short term nature, this too should be obvious from the site inspection. Longer term erosional trends may be caused by structures interfering with the natural supply of sand to the dune area. Such structures could be groynes located some distance from the site or possible underwater obstructions to sand movement. Evaluating the causes of erosion may therefore entail discussions with adjacent landowners, local authorities, harbour authorities, etc.

Any coastal works in the vicinity of the dune system should be examined carefully to see if they may have triggered off downdrift erosion. Changes in the land use should also be considered, including the possibility of trampling, wind induced scour or overgrazing. If the causes of erosion have not been identified a revisit should be made. Discussions should be held with local conservation volunteers, Council engineers, golf course managers, fishermen etc. to obtain background information about the area.

5.6   Measuring the amount of erosion

If erosion is not threatening to create a permanent breach in the dunes, or a serious loss of dune area, no capital works should be considered until a number of site surveys have been made over a period of at least two winters. As noted in the introduction, change to the beach and dunes can occur over a range of timescales. The frequency of surveying must recognise this. Initially surveys should be undertaken bi-monthly, with additional surveys following severe storms. Regular surveys should be completed at the same point in the tidal cycle, e.g. during Spring tides, and post-storm surveys should be completed as close to the event as possible. After the first year (say, six to ten surveys) the frequency can drop to quarterly, plus post storm (say, four to eight surveys). After several years the surveys will have revealed the potential extent of short term change, and the frequency can drop once more to early spring and early autumn, plus extreme storms (say, two to four surveys). The timing of these ongoing surveys should be consistent in terms of the month and the tidal state, perhaps ideally the March equinox tide (erosion expected) and the first Spring tide in September (accretion expected). At this frequency the long term trends can be monitored, and can be analysed with a well founded knowledge of short term variation.

Measurements should give the bearing and distance to identifiable features from each datum. These features will be some or all of the following:

- The seaward limit of the yellow dunes
- The seaward limit of the foredunes
- The scarp slope or any identifiable part of the seaward face of the dune system
- The boundary between different types of dune/beach system (i.e. the transition between dune, shingle upper beach, sand lower foreshore, muddy offshore zone, etc).

Having identified the various geomorphological zones, any change to their extent between successive surveys should be mapped. The horizontal rates of change of the various boundaries can be calculated and put into context. Simple spreadsheet software or survey analysis packages will allow changes to be stored and presented effectively.

5.7 Erosion Checklist

An indication of the severity and possible causes of erosion may be obtained from the following checklist. Note: the values given are indicative only.

Measured Change/Observation	Comments/Possible Causes of Erosion
Less than 1m over a year at all points.	Erosion likely to be insignificant.
Over 1m between surveys.	Erosion may be significant or may be episodic (cyclic).
Erosion of the dune face sustained at 1m per year.	Erosion significant and possibly severe.
Erosion of the dune face at 1m to 10m per year.	Serious erosion requiring immediate attention.
Dunes badly trampled at individual access points.	Localised pedestrian damage.
Dunes badly damaged over large dune area.	Serious damage due to tourist pressure, livestock or vermin.
Discrete areas of dune face erosion.	Wind damage (blow outs).
Dune face erosion over wide area.	Damage by wave action.
Dune toe and upper beach erosion.	Damage caused by waves or tidal currents.
Upper and lower beach accretion.	Change of profiles in response to wave conditions.
Upper and lower beach erosion.	Severe wave erosion/meandering of tidal channel/impact of coastal defence.
Dune scarp/exposure of marram roots.	Sustained recession of dunes.
Dune scarp covered by fresh sand accretion.	Intermittent dune recession.
Beach ridges/runnels moving landwards.	Recent beach build up, hence dune erosion may be temporary.
Beach ridges/runnels moving seawards.	Beach erosion continuing, hence dune recession also likely.
Beach salients.	Unstable conditions in an alongshore direction may result in local and episodic recession in adjacent areas.
Groynes/breakwaters located updrift.	Beach may be affected by downdrift erosion.
River/training walls updrift.	Beach may be affected by a change in sediment supply.
Eroded dune surface but beach stable/backshore sand covered.	Wind induced erosion/pedestrian damage/livestock or vermin damage.
Seawall remnants.	Evidence of long term erosion.
Groynes/seawall, etc. on lower foreshore.	Strong evidence of long term erosion.
Groynes/seawalls/sills at toe of dune but recession continuing.	Inadequate defences/unusually severe wave/tidal conditions.
Groynes/seawalls/sills at toe of dunes but displaced or tilted over.	Unusually severe waves/tidal currents causing structural failure. Possibly poor initial design or poor foundations.
Erosion in one area of beach or sediment cell matched by accretion in adjacent area.	Change in dominant wind/wave direction.
Erosion throughout frontage including non dune areas.	Adjustment to changed wave climate/tidal prism, not related to human activities.
Severe erosion at structure tailing off downdrift.	Lee side erosion caused by coastal works.

6.   Monitoring techniques – aerial photography

As a compliment to the observational and low cost approaches set out in Section 5, the most useful method of monitoring dune morphology changes is by aerial photography. Professionally flown, survey quality, aerial photos provide excellent records of change and are useful for obtaining an overall understanding of dune systems as well as monitoring marine erosion. Hand held photography or video taken from a small plane at low altitude can produce very useful qualitative information. As an alternative there are a number of companies offering the services of model aeroplanes equipped with survey cameras.

Photogrammetric measurements of erosion or accretion require the services of specialist aerial surveyors. Colour photos at a scale of about 1:5000 taken with appropriate overlaps will allow photogrammetric analysis to produce digital ground models, from which changes can be measured (+/-100mm resolution). Photogrammetry requires ground control points that are carefully surveyed for position (x, y, z), visible from the air and can be replaced at the exact position for subsequent flights. There are numerous aerial survey companies around the country who are able to provide a professional service, although it may be difficult to obtain competitive quotes for work in more remote areas. Flights should be undertaken annually and close to the same dates and tidal conditions to allow easy comparison. Clear weather and good light are required for best results. Tide levels should be below mean low water to allow important process information to be derived for the beach as well as the dunes. Where small dune systems are to be monitored it may be sensible to survey several sites during a single flight.

7   Measurements of the physical environment

Monitoring morphological change is useful to maintenance operations, but does not allow for improved forward planning of dune management. Additional meteorological and sea state information is required to understand the processes leading to change.

Some processes are active over a very long term. These include changes in relative sea level, changes in the total volume of sand available to the coast (due to particle degradation, cliff erosion or losses to offshore sinks), or changes in climate. Measurement of these processes is undertaken under regional and national research programmes and can not be effectively addressed at a local level.

Other processes occur over time scales that can be measured, including tides, storm surges, winds and waves. Some, or all, of these may be measured regionally and managers may be able to access the information from port managers, coast guard stations or the Meteorological Office. However, dune systems can be influenced by processes that are site specific: winds are influenced by local topography and exposure directions; storm surges measured at the nearest port tide gauge may be quite different in character within an embayment 60km away; and waves are strongly affected by local wind, bathymetry, currents, and by exposure to the open sea.

If the shoreline manager wants to measure local conditions to help understand specific dune responses, it is quite possible to deploy tide gauges, anemometers and wave monitors. However, the costs for a low maintenance system that can telemeter real time data direct to a shore based PC for processing, analysis and storage will be high, while the quality of data retrieved from a low technology, labour intensive system may be too poor to make the effort worthwhile on a long term basis. Specialist advice on appropriate technology must be sought on a site by site basis.

As an alternative to deploying wave monitors, which are the most costly and difficult of the instruments, it is possible to get high quality predicted wave information from the Met Office for offshore points all around the UK (and Europe). The offshore data can be transferred inshore using a numerical transformation model for analysis in conjunction with observations and aerial mapping.

Tide information can be derived from a regional tide gauge provided that local information is available to determine appropriate time and range corrections. This local information is best obtained by deploying a tide gauge close to the site for a period of at least 4 weeks (two tidal cycles) for comparison with the regional gauge or for computer analysis to determine harmonic constituents. The former is a relatively simple operation and the analysis can be done without specialist help, while harmonic analysis requires appropriate software and knowledge. Analysis will provide adequate data to determine local tide levels, but will not be reliable for storm surges; only long term (i.e. 10 years plus) local measurements will provide information on potential maximum surge elevations.

8   Data Storage and Analysis

Data collected must be stored effectively if it is to serve any long term purpose. Clear records that can be retrieved and interpreted by others should be kept. Spread sheets should contain sufficient header information to be of general use, rather than simply presenting a series of numbers. Full use should be made of comments recorded in field note books, as data analysis may not take place for months or even years after collection, when memories of site observations are no longer reliable.

GIS (Geographical Information Systems) packages offer convenient data storage, analysis and display systems. However, setting up an effective GIS is a specialist and costly task, and requires ongoing management to obtain a useful return in the future. It is likely that a GIS would only be cost effective if maintained on a regional or even national basis, including all of the dune systems of interest in Scotland.

Having collected and processed field data on an apparently eroding dune system, the manager may feel that action is vital to prevent further deterioration. As discussed earlier, unless there is strong evidence that erosion is ongoing over at least several years, it will be prudent to wait before committing to any more than minor maintenance work. The shoreline is a dynamic zone, and erosion can revert to accretion, making the managers efforts redundant.

Dune and Beach Monitoring Proforma

Location		Observed by:	
Grid reference From:		To:	
Date:	Time:	Tide range:	Tide level:

PHYSICAL CHARACTER	COMMENTS
Foreshore	
Sand · Shingle · Sa/Sh Cobbles · Boulders · Rock Salt Marsh · Mud · Shells Other:	
Foreshore Processes	
Eroding · Accreting · Stable Severe · Moderate · Low Wave · Tidal · Wind	
Backshore	
Grey dunes · Yellow dunes Machair · Links Wooded · Grassland Other:	
Backshore processes	
Eroding · Accreting · Stable Severe · Moderate · Low Deflation · Frontal Blowout · Trampling	
Causes	
Waves · Wind · Currents High water levels · Pedestrians Livestock · Vehicles · Rabbits Other:	
CONSERVATION INTERESTS	
SSSI · AGLV · SAC SPA · RAMSAR · NNR LNR · GCR · NCR Other:	
LAND OWNERSHIP/ISSUES	
Residential · Industry Tourist · Conservation Road · Rail Farming · Caravans · Golf Forestry · MOD · Recreation Other:	

Dune and Beach Monitoring

COASTAL DEFENCES		
Re-planting Thatching Fencing		
Beach recycling Sandbags		
Beach recharge Gabions		
Artificial headlands Nearshore breakwaters or reefs		
Groynes Beach drainage		
Rock revetment Timber revetment		
Impermeable revetment Seawall		
Other:		

Condition/Impact	
Good Fair Poor Bad	
Downdrift Drawdown	

Action required	Immediate	< 1 year	< 5 years	> 5 years
Field measurements	Details of measurements, photo, location, etc.			
Photographs Tape survey				
Aerial survey Full survey				

Sketch/Other Notes (include wind speed, wave height, wind direction and wave direction if erosion is active during observation)

Dune and Beach Monitoring - Tape survey record

Shoreline feature	Marker Ref.	Distance from marker	Bearing from marker	Comment